# EVENTS IN SPACE

# EVENTS IN SPACE

## by WILLY LEY

DAVID McKAY COMPANY, INC.   New York

# EVENTS IN SPACE

COPYRIGHT © 1969 BY WILLY LEY

LIBRARY OF CONGRESS CATALOG CARD NUMBER: 69-20204

MANUFACTURED IN THE UNITED STATES OF AMERICA

VAN REES PRESS • NEW YORK

# Contents

# Foreword

SINCE World War II, Willy Ley has been increasingly recognized as a leading historian and archivist in the field of rocketry and space flight, both in this country and abroad. Such he is to the thousands of readers of his books, columns, and articles. For those of us who have worked professionally in these fields, he is more than that. He is "the" reference source on the history of our profession. This recognition is borne out by the award of honorary fellow membership by U.S., British, and German astronautical societies and election to the International Academy of Astronautics.

It seems to me there are three reasons for Willy Ley's preeminence. One is the startling depth of his documentary research, stretching back forty years to the great libraries of Berlin and elsewhere in Europe. Another reason is that Ley was himself one of the organizers of German rocketry, sharing in the excitement, triumphs, frustrations, and despair of experimental tests in the late 1920s and early 1930s. Finally, and particularly important to the reader, Willy Ley is a great story-teller. He tells it like it was, and is, clearly and with wit and humor.

In this book, the story of artificial satellites is engagingly told; how they evolved, who contributed to the technology and how, and the manner in which the stage was set for the traumatic impact of the first Sputnik nearly twelve years ago.

The applications satellites—first useful tools of the space age—are already at work, serving man. Much more capable sophisticated satellites are soon to be launched. The manned space station will become a reality in the next few years.

Willy Ley points out the international quality of new ideas, again and again, proving that no single nation has an exclusive patent on originality.

The careful log of all known satellites launched from 1957 to 1969 is an important and useful reference. The glossaries of satellite and rocket names are a boon to all of us who simply cannot remember the dozens of the changing project names and the original purpose of the programs.

Willy Ley assembles the cast of characters, major and minor, who have had their moment on stage in prologue or the present. The next act will be even more exciting.

F. C. DURANT, III
National Air and Space Museum
Washington, D.C.

15 April 1969

EVENTS IN SPACE

# CHAPTER I

# The Birth of the Satellites

SOME questions sound clear and simple, but they have a major drawback: they have no answer. I do not mean a question where the answer is not known, as, for example, the date of birth of Christopher Columbus. I mean a question that literally has no answer. By way of example I can offer one that has been asked of me a number of times: "Who invented the artificial satellite?"

There is no answer to this question because the question itself assumes that a single man did it. In reality the invention was spread through hundreds of years and as many different brains. It should not even be called an invention.

William R. Corliss, who wrote an account titled *Scientific Satellites* for the National Aeronautics and Space Administration (NASA), divided the history of artificial satellites prior to the first actual shot in 1957 into three phases. The period from 1870 to 1928 he called the "Idea Phase," the time from 1928 to 1945 he called the "Phase of the Amateur Enthusiasts," and the years from 1945 to 1957 the "Phase of Guarded Acceptance." This is a useful subdivision of what went on, but requires some explanations. First, the concept of artificial satellites was already in exist-

1

ence at the beginning of the "Idea Phase." In fact, it was by then almost two hundred years old.

Sir Isaac Newton had given much thought to gravity and the phenomena caused by gravity during the years from 1666 to 1687. He became convinced that one body in space moved around another body for two reasons, namely gravitational attraction on the one hand and the inertia of a moving body on the other hand. If a body is at rest, it will stay at rest unless some force is applied to change this condition. Similarly, if a body is in motion, it will stay in motion unless some force acts upon it to stop its motion. This was his definition of inertia, now also called Newton's First Law of Motion.

Newton then continued his reasoning as follows: If there were no other force than inertia, the bodies in the universe would just move along straight lines, but observation shows that they do not, hence there must be a second force present. The second force, of course, was gravity. Newton, at that point, investigated a side issue. The earth is a very large body, but no matter where you are on earth the vertical line—any piece of string with a weight at its end—always points toward the center of the earth. Could one assume, for the purposes of calculation, that the gravity of the earth behaved as if all the mass of the earth were concentrated in its center? He believed that one could calculate gravitational attraction in this manner, and then he was ready to explain why the moon moves around the earth.

By about the year 1680 all this was perfectly clear in Newton's mind, but then a new problem came up: How could he explain his reasoning to others? He finally had a diagram drawn (Fig. 1), in which he explained the motion of the moon by using artificial satellites. The diagram shows the earth with a very high mountain which serves only the purpose of being a firing platform for a cannon

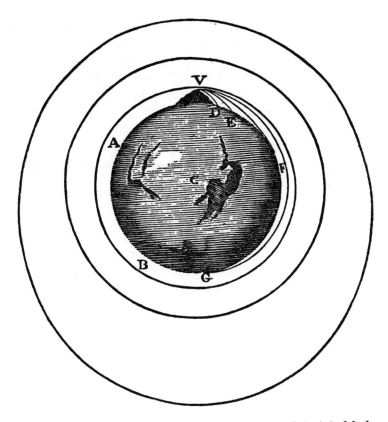

Fig. 1. The diagram from Sir Isaac Newton's *Principia Mathematica* which introduced the concept of artificial satellites.

above the atmosphere. Newton knew that any actual experiment would be ruined by air resistance. Hence he placed his cannon above the atmosphere, saw to it that the barrel was strictly horizontal, and fired a cannonball which, he said, under the influence of gravity would strike the ground some distance away. The second shot was then to be fired with more gunpowder in the barrel so that the

**3**

cannonball would acquire a higher velocity. It would still fall to the ground, but a longer distance away.

The faster the cannonball left the muzzle of the barrel, the farther it would travel. It might go a quarter of the way around the earth, or halfway around the earth, or even all the way around the earth. Three conditions had to be met: (1) the cannonball must move above the atmosphere, (2) it must be fast enough, and (3) it must be fired horizontally, or, as Newton expressed it, "parallel to the horizon."

It begins to look at this point as if Sir Isaac Newton could qualify as the "inventor" of artificial satellites. Actually he doesn't, of course, because the experiment could never be performed the way he explained it, if only for the lack of a mountain with its peak outside the atmosphere. Moreover, Newton's "use" of cannonballs for artificial satellites only had the purpose of making clear why the moon orbits the earth. And though Newton had supplied the concept of an artificial satellite, nobody ever considered it anything but a "thought experiment," as reasoning of this type came to be called.

The book in which our Fig. 1 appeared for the first time is now known as *Newton's Principia*. Published in 1687, it was printed in Latin, as Newton had written it, but translations into English and other modern languages followed very soon.

Now the idea existed, and soon an artificial satellite was mentioned for the first time in fiction. The story, called "The Brick Moon," appeared in three installments in the last three issues for the year 1869 in the *Atlantic Monthly*. Its author was the Boston clergyman Edward Everett Hale. Unfortunately, nobody can tell whether the Reverend Mr. Hale had taken the idea from Newton's work or whether he had thought of it himself. The story itself can be summed up easily. A large and hollow spherical structure, built of bricks, is to be launched into an orbit around the earth as an aid for navigation for small seagoing craft; unfortunately it is launched by accident before it could be painted white (for better visibility) and while there are still workmen inside the structure.

The next fiction writer to mention an artificial satellite was Jules Verne, in 1879, in a story that is known under several titles. It is called "Steel City" by one translator, "The Five Hundred Millions of the Begum" by a more careful translator, and "The Five Hundred Million of the Indian Princess" by a third translator, who thought that the readers might not know what a "begum" was. At any event, the very large fortune of the Indian princess falls in equal shares to two men, one French, one German. The Frenchman uses the money to build a model city; the German uses his to build a steelmaking industrial city. Verne was quite unhappy at the time over the outcome of the war of 1870–71 between France and Germany, so he made the German the villain who finally decides to get rid of the happy model city of his French co-heir by destroying it with one shot from a super-gun. The gun is built and fired, but the muzzle velocity of the projectile was too high, so that it passes over the model city and becomes an artificial satellite.

Artificial satellites next made their appearance in a work of fiction published in 1897, and its author was a German professor of mathematics Kurd Lasswitz. *Auf zwei Planeten* (On Two Planets) has unfortunately never been translated; and the two planets in question are the earth and Mars. At that time it seemed very likely that the planet Mars might be inhabited, and both Lasswitz in Germany and H. G. Wells in England reasoned that the Martians, if their civilization was older than ours, would come to us instead of

5

our going to Mars. While Wells (in his *War of the Worlds* published in 1898) simply has the Martian space vessels crash on earth, Lasswitz constructed his Martian spacecraft along mathematical principles.

Spaceships, he reasoned, would probably not do well in an atmosphere. Hence the Martian ships would not land on earth, but would land on a space station from which the Martians would reach the ground by way of shuttle craft. (Note that this is the actual method we are now using to land on the moon.) Moreover, Lasswitz decided, it would be impractical to adjust the shuttle craft to the rotation of the earth. Therefore the Martian space stations are placed over the poles of the earth so that the shuttle craft land at the earth's poles in centers built for this purpose.

Everybody now knows that a space station could not just hang over the pole but would have to orbit the earth. Without movement, it would fall to earth at once. Lasswitz knew this, too, but for story purposes he could not have an orbiting space station, because astronomers on earth would detect it very soon. Hence Lasswitz made the assumption that his Martians had succeeded in learning about the nature of gravity and that the space stations were held in their places by a manipulation of the earth's gravitational field.

Those who eagerly read Lasswitz's novel or Wells's *War of the Worlds* did not know that the theme of space travel was just beginning to approach reality. A few people felt that engineering, which had made such wonderful strides all through the nineteenth century, should be about ready to tackle the problem of going into space.

Space was acquiring its first scientific prophets during the last decade of the nineteenth century, and it so happened that the first of these prophets were two imaginative men as different from each other as possible. They even lived in surroundings as different as possible—one in a suburb of the splendid imperial capital of Germany, the other in a small town, named Kaluga, in the district of Perm of the Russian Empire. The German was named Hermann Ganswindt, and the Russian was Konstantin Eduardovitch Tsiolkovsky. It is difficult to decide which of the two should be discussed first; Ganswindt made his ideas known earlier than Tsiolkovsky, but on the other hand, Tsiolkovsky exerted more influence later on. The overall result is that Ganswindt's story is shorter, so let's begin with him.

He was born in East Prussia on June 12, 1856, and his parents were of the opinion that little Hermann, after grade school and high school, should study law at the University of Berlin. Of course they thought that, after having passed his exams, he would apply for a government position and possibly become a judge. But if he disappointed his parents by going into private practice as a lawyer, they were willing to forgive him. A well-known lawyer is an asset to a family, too. Ganswindt did disappoint his parents, but in a manner nobody had foreseen. As a student (he was tall as a young man and quite heavy later in his life) the black-eyed and black-haired Hermann Ganswindt was a great reader. However, he read books on law and famous court decisions only when he had to. Most of his reading consisted of books on inventions, on physics and mechanics. Fine legal points did not interest him at all; the fine points of a mechanical device were what he really liked. At the age of about twenty he made his decision to leave the university and become an inventor.

He did become one—not great, for he lacked the necessary patience for that, but certainly versatile. He invented an early version of the free-wheeling mechanism of the bicycle. He invented a device by which a light carriage could be moved by the driver (who stood behind the passengers) by shifting his weight rhythmically from one foot to the other. He invented a helicopter which would have flown if he had been able to find a sufficiently light and powerful engine. That his helicopter would not have been stable is something that neither he nor anybody else could have figured out at the time. He drew up plans for a dirigible that might have worked if it had been built, and he made a design sketch for a spaceship that would not have worked, even though it was based on the rocket principle. And he said (which is what interests us here) that his spaceships could orbit the earth without any fuel expenditure. In short, he had the right idea, even though his proposals for making his ideas work were faulty.

It is possible that Ganswindt, in time and with the assistance of professional engineers, could have made several of his inventions work, but he never had enough money for true research and development. Slowly, interest in his ideas faded out; a number of unfortunate lawsuits did not help. Though he lived until 1934, the last thirty years of his life were unimportant. Berliners who had known about him in the days of his glory considered him just a bit of local history, somewhat like a famous aging actress or singer. Only after his death on October 25 did his name appear in the newspapers once more.

While Ganswindt had all the advantages of a big city—libraries, museums, and experts whom one could ask for advice about specific points—Tsiolkovsky had none of them. But he was the better thinker. Ganswindt actually put pieces of metal together, but Tsiolkovsky evolved theories and wrote equations.

He was born one year after Ganswindt, on September 17, 1857. This date is according to our calendar, which came into use in Russia only after the Bolshevik revolution. At the time he was born, Russians still used the older Julian calendar, so that his birth certificate bore the date of September 5, 1857. His father was a forester by profession and a Pole by ancestry; his mother was Russian. The family never went hungry, but there was no money for anything that in a small Russian town at that time might be considered a luxury, such as books. Even so, it would have been difficult to buy books, other than fiction, in such a small town. To make life even more difficult, Tsiolkovsky, as a boy, fell sick with typhus. He survived, but was nearly deaf ever after.

In spite of these problems he managed to be a good pupil and studied for the teaching profession. After he had passed his exams and acquired a poorly paid job, he began both to think and to write. While Ganswindt tried to take in the whole field of engineering, Tsiolkovsky had only one dream: to go into space. He soon realized that rockets were the only means to do so, and he wrote to a friend that he had a "super rocket" in mind. He also wrote to another friend that there was only coarse black bread in his stomach, but his brain was full of the most wonderful ideas.

In 1903 his first treatise on space travel was published, as the main article in a magazine *Time and People*. It was Tsiolkovsky's bad luck that this particular issue also contained a political article which the censors of the Czar did not like, so the whole edition was confiscated. Tsiolkovsky continued his work, however, and in 1910, he completed a paper that he considered "Part II," containing an introduction that condensed the confiscated article of the year 1903. The new, very long article appeared in 1911 in an aviation journal, *Messenger of Flight*, that had not existed in 1903, one devoted only to aviation. This journal at least did not have any political troubles.

But since it was printed in Russian, the knowledge of Tsiolkovsky's space-travel ideas and even of Tsiolkovsky's existence was restricted to Russia. When the American physicist Robert H. Goddard began thinking about rockets in 1911 or 1912, he had no idea that a Russian schoolteacher had already evolved much of the theory.

In Russia Tsiolkovsky's fame spread, mainly through the efforts of a physicist who liked to write for the public. His name was Dr. Yakov Isidorovitch Perelman, and he was what we would call science editor of several newspapers in succession. His articles were then collected in book form and apparently were widely read. In 1923 the Soviet government had Tsiolkovsky's article of 1903 reprinted as a pamphlet, and all the other writings of Tsiolkovsky were also reprinted as pamphlets in the years to come. When he turned seventy-five in 1932 there was a big official celebration of his birthday. A medal was awarded to him; newspapers published full-page articles about him; and when he died, on September 19, 1935, he received a state funeral and a monument was erected in Kaluga, where he had spent most of his life.

Twenty years after his death, the Soviets decided that they would orbit their first artificial satellite on September 17, 1957, the hundredth anniversary of Tsiolkovsky's birth. But the timetable could not be quite met; the first launch was about two and a half weeks late. Still later, after Soviet cosmonauts had orbited the earth, the Cosmonaut Medal showed Tsiolkovsky's likeness, he was pictured on several Russian postage stamps, a crater on the moon's farside was named after him, and a second monument was erected in Moscow. There, on a public square, is an enormous glittering monument to the cosmonauts, showing a rocket on top of a stylized exhaust blast; the exhaust blast glitters because it is covered with the "space-age metal" titanium. And in front of this monument there is the monument to Tsiolkovsky, showing him seated in an armchair.

Before we can go on to Goddard, another early Russian

has to be mentioned: Professor Ivan Meshtchersky of the Polytechnic Institute in St. Petersburg, now called Leningrad. In 1903 Professor Meshtchersky published a textbook for students of physics and of engineering. He called it *Collection of Problems in Theoretical Mechanics,* and it was a book that practically every engineering student in Russia read at one time. Nobody then paid much attention to one of Professor Meshtchersky's problems, which dealt with trajectories and orbits around the earth. But after the first artificial satellites were in orbit, somebody realized that while Tsiolkovsky had supplied the idea, Meshtchersky had supplied the mathematical methods.

The whole story of Russian contributions during the Idea Phase shows quite clearly that the Russians were quite independent then. As we shall see, they continued to be independent.

In the Western countries the Idea Phase bore fruit somewhat later than in Russia, but four different people in four different countries began to think about space at the same time. The period in question was the First World War, a time, interestingly enough, during which the Russians made no progress at all.

In order of their birth the four men were:

Dr. Walter Hohmann, 1880–1944, engineer, German
Robert Esnault-Pelterie, 1881–1957, engineer, French
Robert H. Goddard, 1882–1945, physicist, American
Hermann Oberth, born 1894, mathematician, Austrian, later German

Dr. Walter Hohmann, born in a small town in the district of Odenwald in western Germany, went from a technical university to jobs in industry, but then applied for a position with the government of the city of Essen and advanced to the rank of City Architect. Quiet and methodical in everything, he read an astronomy book in 1912 and became interested in the mechanics of orbits of celestial bodies. Though quiet and methodical, he did not lack imagination and began to wonder about the "routes" or orbits of artificial satellites connecting the orbits of celestial bodies. He began a systematic study of this thought and drew two diagrams, one showing the orbits of earth and Mars and the other showing the orbits of earth and Venus. He then connected the actual orbits in these diagrams by five different "routes" (or orbits) of assumed spaceships traveling from earth to Mars and from earth to Venus.

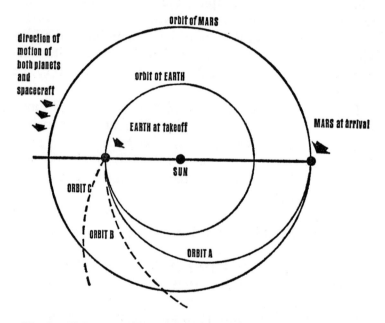

Fig. 2. Hohmann's Diagram. Orbit C would cross both the orbits of earth and of Mars, orbit B would touch the orbit of earth but cross that of Mars, while orbit A touches both the orbits of earth and of Mars. Orbit A, which takes the longest time but is the most economical with regard to fuel consumption, is now called "the Hohmann."

12

That done, he calculated what the transit times of these assumed "routes" would be, and how much fuel would be consumed in getting from one planet to the other. He then drew up tables, listing the probable weight of the structure, the amounts of food and water required for two people, and so forth. When he was done, he had proved to himself that of the five possible "routes" the one that only touched the orbits of the two planets in question, but did not cross either of them, was the most efficient in one respect—it required the least fuel consumption. It also happened to require the longest time. But Hohmann felt that fuel consumption was the main item, and he felt that this particular "route" or orbit (he had labeled it A) was the most likely one to be used.

By the time he had completed his study, the year was 1916 and Europe was just entering the third year of the First World War. Hohmann decided that this was the wrong time to publish a book on the theme of possible orbits for possible spaceships and put his manuscript away. In 1924 he took it off the shelf and added a few more figures; in 1925 one could hope for more powerful rocket fuels than one could have expected in 1916. With this additional material the book was published in 1925. It sold very poorly, but it was one of the more important milestones on the road to space travel. Dr. Hohmann remained in his adopted city until his death in 1944 when he was killed in an Allied bombing raid. No government ever put his picture on a stamp or erected a monument to him.

But the Orbit A which he had worked out is now called "the Hohmann" by NASA.

Robert Esnault-Pelterie, the French space pioneer, was born in Paris November 8, 1881, and he was the third-generation Esnault-Pelterie to become an officer of the *Légion d'honneur*. His father, Albert Henri, and his grandfather,

Augustus Emanuel, had been accorded the same honor. Both his father and his grandfather had been rich cotton merchants, but Robert was after something else. He wanted to fly, and, as a student, expected to be hailed as "the first man to fly a heavier-than-air machine"—an airplane. He studied the physical sciences at the old University of Paris and graduated in 1901. Then he began to experiment systematically with kite shapes. He built a glider and took a lesson from his kite experiments; gliders, like kites, need wind to fly, but a boy can run with a kite if there is no wind.

As Robert Esnault-Pelterie could afford to buy an automobile, he bought the heaviest type in existence at the time. Then he hired a driver for the car while he sat in the towed glider, piloting it. At about that time he began to refer to himself by his initials REP. While REP was not the first to fly, he did build an exceptionally good airplane, making several patentable inventions in the course of his work.

As soon as he had a good airplane, he began to think about space travel, delivering a lecture on space travel to the French Physical Society in November 1912. This lecture, which was printed a year later, makes very interesting reading nowadays, because it is a mixture of good predictions with wrong conclusions. He said that spaceships must be rocket-propelled, and that the most powerful chemical fuel is a mixture of hydrogen and oxygen.* But he went on to maintain that even this powerful fuel was not powerful enough to get man to the planets. The only source of power that could do that would be radium, if one could control the rate at which it changes into other elements. In short, he had atomic energy in mind in 1912! During the war years

* Theoretically, hydrogen and fluorine would make a more powerful mixture, but at the time very little was known about fluorine. Hydrogen and oxygen are now in use in the American Centaur rocket, but the French *Centaure* rocket is a solid-fuel rocket.

14

he was busy supplying airplanes, but he thought about space even then, and slowly he changed his mind. Rockets with chemical fuels should be at least good enough to explore the upper atmosphere of the earth.

By 1927 he had read the books of Walter Hohmann and Hermann Oberth. Apparently he knew German well, as his letters to me in Germany, when handwritten, were not only in German but even in German script. His typed letters were in French. He put together everything he knew on the subject and published a small book. Its title, rendered into English, was *The Exploration of the Upper Atmosphere by Rockets and the Possibility of Interplanetary Voyages.* After that, with the banker André Hirsch, he established the annual REP-Hirsch Prize for Astronautics. (It was REP who coined the word "astronautics.") The man who won the prize for the first time was Hermann Oberth. Then REP wrote a much bigger book entitled *l'Astronautique* (1930) and became a prizewinner himself; he won a prize from one French society and a gold medal from another one.

REP now began to build a liquid-fuel rocket designed to carry scientific instruments to an altitude of 60 miles. From what has become known about this rocket, it probably would have been successful, but REP was due for a streak of bad luck. First he lost several fingers of one hand in an explosion. By the time he was ready to continue his work, the Second World War had started and the Germans marched into Paris.

He was then sixty years old, felt generally sick, and had a heart condition. He wanted to move to Geneva for treatment by a doctor there whom he knew and trusted. The Germans let him go; they were not interested in a man too old for work and sick, too. His Swiss doctor suggested one more move: to Majorca, where the climate would be good for him. REP lived there for 17 years and finally died in a

**15**

hospital in Nice on December 6, 1957. He is buried in Paris, in the cemetery known as the Père Lachaise.

Robert H. Goddard, the American rocket pioneer, was born in Worcester, Massachusetts, on October 5, 1882. Two years later the family moved to Boston. As a boy he was sick so often that he fell behind in school, and his doctor finally had him removed from school and brought to his grandmother's farm. The complete rest did what was expected. Young Robert recovered enough to be enrolled at the Worcester Polytechnic Institute in 1904, where he received his M.A. in 1910. His main interest at the time was electricity. For relaxation he read H. G. Wells's *War of the Worlds,* and from then on, his thinking was about space. Being a physicist, he knew that only a rocket could furnish propulsion in a vacuum, and he began to think about the shape these rockets should have.

This was in 1913, and unfortunately Goddard had much time to think. He had fallen sick again, and his doctor could not doubt what was wrong with him: tuberculosis in both lungs. Against his doctor's expectations, Goddard recovered, and he applied for two patents. Both were granted. They were the first two of over a hundred patents Goddard was to obtain, and both dealt with rockets. The first described a rocket for solid fuels to be used in the manner of a machine gun. Later Goddard spent a great deal of time trying to make such a rocket work, but he never succeeded. In the other patent a rocket for liquid fuels is mentioned as a side issue; the fuels described in the patent were never used by anybody, not even by Goddard himself. It is probable that he used them just as an example, not as something he wanted to try.

During the First World War Goddard refined and extended his theory; as a professor at Clark University he could use the laboratory facilities for making some experiments. When he had finished his paper, he sent it off to the Smithsonian Institution asking for a research grant so that he could continue experimenting. To his surprise the Smithsonian not only gave him a grant, but also offered to publish his paper after a few necessary revisions were made. It was printed in 1919 under the title of "A Method of Reaching Extreme Altitudes." As the title indicates, Goddard spoke mainly of rockets as a means of exploring the upper atmosphere, but there was an appendix about the possibility of shooting an unmanned rocket to the moon.

Many years later, after his death, columnists began to write weepy articles about Goddard, saying that the government never paid any attention to him and his ideas, that his neighbors ridiculed him, and that he never had a friendly press. The only fact that is true is that his neighbors ridiculed him, as they admitted with shame later on. But the government was always willing to listen to Goddard and gave him financial support on occasion, the occasion being weapons development. During the period between the two World Wars the U.S. Government showed so little interest in science that one can say it showed none. It was not even too willing to spend money for armament, but as this could not be completely avoided, Goddard got one or two of the small contracts that were given out. Nor is it true that he had an unfriendly press. There had been an uninformed and ridiculing article about him in the very beginning where one would expect it least, namely, in *The New York Times*. But afterwards the papers were only too willing to print what Goddard told them. Unfortunately, he hardly ever told them anything.

Goddard was secretive and suspicious by choice and was inimical to anybody who was not born in the United States. For a scientist, this is a strange attitude indeed, as the next discovery might be made by somebody called Polyakoff, or

Tuyikava, or Gerstenfeld. Goddard's first paper (he only published one more, a sixteen-page report on some later experiments) was not the foundation on which the space age was built. But Robert H. Goddard was the first man to build a liquid-fuel rocket and to fire it—on March 16, 1926, from a farm near Auburn in Massachusetts. (It is also true that he kept this accomplishment secret for years to come.)

He was the first, and no personal eccentricities can diminish that fact.

About Goddard's later work more is to be said in the next chapter, but his personal history must be summarized here. He moved to New Mexico to work, with financial support from both the Guggenheim and the Carnegie Foundations. During the Second World War the Navy (for which he had done some work before) called him to Annapolis to work on rockets that were to help heavily loaded flying boats take off. There he died August 10, 1945, of cancer of the throat. Much honor came to his name posthumously, and two professorships are named after him, one at Princeton University and one at the California Institute of Technology. The Navy named a power plant near Annapolis after him, and NASA named its space flight center at Greenbelt, Maryland, the Goddard Space Flight Center. His picture appeared on a U.S. postage stamp. And the American Rocket Society placed a granite marker on the field near Auburn where the first liquid-fuel rocket had lifted itself off the ground.

And now we come to Hermann Oberth.

He was born on June 25, 1894, in a city which was then called Hermannstadt and which was then the capital of a district called Siebenbürgen (Seven Mountains), a part of the Austro-Hungarian Empire. Now the city is called Sibiu and is a part of Rumania. His father was the local doctor, and it was assumed that Hermann, the firstborn, would become a doctor, too. At first, things seemed to follow this plan, but two events intervened. During his last year in high school, Hermann Oberth fell ill with scarlet fever and was left in a weakened condition. He did graduate, but his father decided that he should have a long vacation before his medical studies began. Hermann was sent to Italy to recover and to dream—the latter not a part of his father's program. Hermann had read Jules Verne's *From the Earth to the Moon* and Lasswitz's *Auf zwei Planeten* and had thought long and hard about both books. By the time he graduated he had not only decided that spaceships should be possible, but had also come to the conclusion that they should be liquid-fuel rockets. During his long vacation he thought of details of construction.

In 1913 he reported to the University of Munich. Of course, his main study was to be medicine, but he attended all kinds of lectures, as was customary in German universities, and had to fight with the thought that he found mathematics more interesting than medicine.

Then came the second event that interfered with his medical career: the First World War. Oberth was drafted into the Austrian army as an infantryman and was transferred to the medical corps after somebody found the time to read his personal file. It so happened that he never saw any front-line duty, and the overall outcome was a "massive dose of boredom," as he later told me more than once. He used his spare time to think about his rockets, and since there was a war going on, he wondered whether such rockets could not be used like artillery. It should be possible to reach a range of about 60 miles and to carry a warhead weighing a thousand pounds, if not more. Oberth calculated and drew plans, but by the time he was finished, Austria and Germany were so close to having lost the war that nobody was interested anymore. (Precisely the same thing happened to Goddard, except that his country was on the winning side.)

After the war Oberth attended the University of Heidelberg, famous for its medical department. Here Oberth heard the lectures of Professor Max Wolf, the famous astronomer. He re-worked his intended 60-mile missile into a rocket for the exploration of the upper atmosphere, and called it his Model B. But he went beyond that; he had a Model E in mind, a man-carrying rocket for two men—the term "astronaut" did not yet exist. And he continued the reasoning that a very large version of the Model E would be left in orbit around the earth, while the men returned to the ground by means of a small rocket vehicle. Oberth wrote about this in incredible detail; every step of his reasoning was provided with a mathematical foundation. He even had a few chapters of medical considerations, investigating the question of whether men could survive a trip into space.

When he was finished, he submitted his manuscript to Professor Wolf as a doctoral dissertation. Wolf told him that he could not accept it as a dissertation because this work dealt with problems in different sciences, all kinds of sciences, but not astronomy. (Professor Wolf would have been surprised to learn, if he had lived long enough, that the thesis he rejected started a new era in astronomy.) Oberth was disappointed, of course, but he had to admit that it was not an astronomical thesis he had written. Wolf, however, wrote a note saying that he had found the manuscript to be scientifically correct.

Oberth, a few years later, had his work printed in Munich, sharing the expenses of printing it with the publisher. The title of the book was *Die Rakete zu den Planetenräumen* (The Rocket into Interplanetary Space). The year was 1923. There is no doubt now that this is the book on which the space age is founded, but for a year or so it attracted little attention.

Meanwhile, something important, but unnoticed at the time, had happened in Russia. A man by the name of Friedrich Arturovitch Tsander (which sounds as if a German were firmly trying to be Russian) had read first Dr. Perelman's writings about Tsiolkovsky, then Tsiolkovsky's own writing, and then parts of Oberth's book. He decided that Russia should take the leading role in the exploration of space. Tsander had been born in Latvia when it was still part of the Russian Empire; this incidentally explains his name, for there were many German names in the areas near the shores of the Baltic Sea. Tsander tried to gain an audience with the Bolshevik leader who called himself Nikolai Lenin and finally succeeded. Lenin was very much interested in all intellectual matters and probably thought of the request as a diversion—he was quite a sick man at the time and actually died a year later. But what had been granted as a ten-minute interlude grew into a long discussion. Lenin promised Tsander that he would be supplied with men and material. Precisely what orders Lenin gave at the time is not known, but Tsander was supplied with men and material. Russian rocket research was underway, though at a very slow pace.

# CHAPTER II

# The Building of the First Rockets

THE year 1926 was a turning point, but not because of Goddard's first shot, which was not publicized at the time. What was important was that all the fundamental books had been printed by then and could be bought in bookstores or consulted in libraries.

The books said what might be built; the next step obviously was to try to build such rockets. This would take some time, as the idea of space travel was by no means popular yet, especially not in the United States. The attitude that space travel was at best a theme for fiction first changed in Europe, especially in the German-speaking countries. This was not so much because two of the main works had been written in German. To anybody not a physicist or an engineer, they were so unreadable that they might just as well have been written in Sanskrit. The change in attitude came through a few people who could understand the scientific works and write popular accounts in magazines or small books.

The first of these popularizers was a fairly young man,

Max Valier. Though the name sounds French, he was actually a native of Bozen in Austria. When in high school Max Valier made up his mind to become an astronomer and wrote a poem in praise of winter because the sky is clearest then. However, the First World War ruined Valier's intended career, too. He was drafted and late in the war found himself attached to the flying corps, where he served as a photographer in reconnaissance aircraft. He was proud of the fact that he had gone through the whole war without ever firing a shot, except during training on the rifle range. After the war he lived mainly in Munich, trying to earn a living as a writer and lecturer on astronomical topics. As a lecturer he began to realize that often there were no definite answers to questions he was asked. Of course, Valier had a favorite explanation in many cases, but he had to admit that other explanations existed and that one often could not say: This is the true answer. When he read Oberth's book he realized that a new possibility had come into being; if spaceships could be built one could just go to another planet and find out.

Thus Valier became an indefatigable prophet of the ships that would one day carry men into space. Collaborating by mail with Oberth, who then lived in Rumania, he wrote a popular book. Articles by him appeared in virtually all the popular magazines. There was one drawback. The magazines, as well as his book publisher, wanted illustrations that showed, among other things, how these spaceships would look. Valier soon found in Munich the brothers von Römer, one of them an architect, the other an artist. They provided him with pictures that had a certain flair, but often did not show what Oberth described. Some were even faintly ridiculous.

It was Valier who was indirectly responsible for the next step forward. One evening, at a large private party in

Munich, Valier delivered a short and enthusiastic lecture on future space travel, saying that the problem ahead was to find money for Oberth so that he could start experimenting. After the lecture a man approached Valier, introduced himself as a lawyer, and told him roughly the following: "Herr Valier, I don't believe a word of all the nonsense about space travel that you have spouted. And if it should be true, I couldn't care less. But let me give you a word of legal advice. If you want to raise money for this and not get into trouble with the law, neither you nor Professor Oberth must accept contributions. You have to found a chartered society for soliciting funds."

Valier had no idea of how to go about having a society chartered. He also had no time, because of his lecture program. One of these lectures was in Breslau, and after the lecture a short and grave gentleman by the name of Johannes Winkler introduced himself and told Valier that he was deeply interested in the subject and was waiting for an opportunity to do something useful. The conversation with the lawyer in Munich flashed back into Valier's mind, and he told Winkler about it. Winkler promised that he would find out about the legalities.

He did, and early in July 1927 the official founding meeting of the new society took place in Breslau, and statutes and by-laws were submitted to the local court. The court raised an absolutely unexpected objection. The name of the society was *Verein für Raumschiffahrt* (Society for Space Travel; I am the last living founding member). The court refused a charter because the word *Raumschiffahrt* (space travel) was not in the dictionary and prospective members therefore would not know what the purpose of this society was supposed to be. It was finally agreed to write a preamble to the statutes in which the meaning of the word was clearly defined.

While the reason for founding the society had been to find a way of raising funds for Professor Oberth, it had the interesting by-product of providing a focal point for everybody interested in the problem. Nor did the VfR, as it soon came to be called, attract only Germans. Citizens of other countries joined, too, and in 1929 the membership roster showed members of eleven different nationalities. Soon foreign members of the VfR began to found similar societies in their own countries. The first was the Austrian Society for High-Altitude Exploration, founded by Dr. Franz von Hoefft and Guido, Baron von Pirquet. Dr. von Hoefft was a chemist; Baron von Pirquet was an engineer with a passion for astronomical calculations.

In March 1930 the American Interplanetary Society was founded in New York by G. Edward Pendray and David Lasser. At that time a society already existed, in Russia, called GIRD, the initials of the Russian words for "Group for the Investigation of Motion by Reaction." There were two branches, one in Leningrad and one in Moscow, referred to as the Lengird and the Mosgird. In 1933 Phil E. Cleator of Liverpool founded the British Interplanetary Society, which after some time was transferred to London. George Bernard Shaw was one of its early members, as was Olaf Stapledon. Another early, but not yet famous, member was Arthur C. Clarke.

The purpose of these various societies was not the same. Originally the VfR had intended only to raise money for experimentation by Prof. Oberth, but it ended up doing experimentation on its own. The American Interplanetary Society * also intended to experiment and did so on a small

* About five years after its founding the American Interplanetary Society changed its name to American Rocket Society (ARS) and many years later, in 1963, merged with the Institute of the Aeronautical Sciences (IAS) to form the American Institute of Aero-

scale for a while. The British Interplanetary Society could never even consider experimentation because of the Guy Fawkes Law preventing the use of explosives. Mosgird and Lengird were organized to study but not to experiment, which was the task of Tsander's group. A few years later Mosgird and Tsander's group became so intermixed that even Russian historians cannot quite straighten out what happened and when.

The year 1928 was an active one. Some time in the spring, Tsander built his first rocket motors, but testing seems to have been postponed. During that year Germany turned into the most rocket-minded country, in part because of Max Valier. Valier had had a chance to talk to Fritz von Opel, the owner of a large automobile factory, and had suggested to von Opel that they develop a rocket motor for liquid fuels. He maintained that this might lead to a new type of airplane, and hinted that Germany's largest automobile manufacturer might expand into the field of aviation. Fritz von Opel seemed to agree, but wanted to know whether rockets could propel an automobile. Valier replied that this would be inefficient (to be efficient a rocket-propelled device must travel at a speed that is near the exhaust velocity of the gases of the rocket) but he indicated that it could be done if the rockets were powerful enough. Opel told Valier to find a manufacturer for powerful rockets, and Valier contacted a factory for naval signal rockets in Wesermünde, owned and operated by the engineer Friedrich Wilhelm Sander.

---

nautics and Astronautics (AIAA). Another society, founded in 1952, the American Astronautical Society, remained independent. None of the societies runs experiments nowadays, but there is an experimenting society for young people, the National Association of Rocketry (NAR).

The sad truth is that Valier was serious, though mistaken in some of his ideas, while Fritz von Opel was then interested in experiments, run at comparatively low expense, which would produce a great deal of publicity for his cars and himself. The first test, using Sander's most powerful signal rockets and a production Opel car, were conducted on March 12 at Rüsselsheim, where the Opel works were located. A racing model without engine was then used and the "rocket-propelled automobile" was demonstrated to the press on April 11. On May 23 there was a public demonstration with a still bigger car and Fritz von Opel behind the wheel on the Avus speedway near Berlin.

By that time Valier began to understand that von Opel was not interested in a new field of engineering and withdrew in disgust. Von Opel had a railroad flatcar equipped with rockets in order to establish a speed record for railbound vehicles. The unmanned vehicle derailed on June 23 and was destroyed by the explosion of the still unburned rockets.

Meanwhile, the first flight with rocket assistance had taken place on June 11. It was an experiment carried out by a glider society called the Rhön-Rossitten Society * and consisted of a glider with two powerful Sander rockets. The glider was put aloft by the then customary method of using a rubber rope, and the rockets were ignited one by one. All went well, except that the glider caught fire after landing.

By the end of the year Professor Nikolai Alekseyevitch Rynin, the head of the Lengird, published the first volume of his nine-volume space encyclopedia. Rynin taught at the same institute where Meshtchersky had been professor of engineering.

* The name was derived from the Rhön mountains in West Germany and Rossitten, a small town in East Prussia where the society maintained two centers of gliding activity.

1928 had been quite noisy, but no real progress had been made.

1929 was somewhat better.

Friedrich Wilhelm Sander, who had been convinced all along that his were the best rockets in existence, began to have second thoughts. If one could build even better rockets, he would build them. He began to work on rockets that used smokeless powder (cordite) as the propelling charge, and even constructed one for liquid fuels. The oxidizer was nitric acid, while the fuel seems to have been fuel oil. He demonstrated both types to government officials and the press on April 10, 1929, but nothing was heard of his work later. Sander, after all, was running a business for profit and realized that it would be years before there was a demand for new types of rockets.

In August 1929 a few interesting experiments were made near Dessau, where the Junkers Airplane Company was located. At the suggestion of Johannes Winkler, Professor Hugo Junkers, chief of the firm, used batteries of rockets to make overloaded pontoon aircraft take off. The experiments worked well, but Junkers kept quiet. He was in business, too, and takeoff assistance by means of rockets might become commercially important at a later date.

During the early part of that year Fritz von Opel seems to have mulled over what Valier had told him about rocket-propelled aircraft. He had a light airplane built, bought more rockets from Sander, and flew the aircraft on September 30. It took off under its own rocket power, but caught fire in flight. Fritz von Opel succeeded in landing the burning craft and in getting out unharmed. It is understandable that he never did it again.

During the later part of the year Max Valier found financial support from the Shell Oil Company and began to work in Berlin in a factory that produced compressed and liquid gases for industry. Its owner and chief scientist was Dr. Paul Heylandt. One of Heylandt's engineers, Walter J. H. Riedel, helped Valier with the development of a liquid-fuel rocket engine which, of course, would use Shell oil as the fuel. Before Valier could show what he had done, another event took place which seemed to have very little to do with science but which was to have lasting influence.

The event was the premiere of a film, on October 15, 1929.

*Frau im Mond* * directed by Fritz Lang, with scientific supervision by Professor Hermann Oberth, was a story of a flight to the moon, with some international intrigue thrown in to increase dramatic tension. The spaceship shown was not some "artist's conception" but a design by Oberth. He had calculated all the dimensions, and the model shown in the movie was a precise scale model. Because of a dramatic requirement—the director wanted a full moon in the sky during takeoff—the flight path that Oberth calculated turned out to be the figure-8 flight path actually taken by Apollo 8. One of the film shots of the lunar surface during the approach of the spacecraft looked precisely like one of the TV transmissions made from Apollo 8. The movie even used the countdown; in fact, the countdown was invented for that movie.

Some of the money from the film was made available for experimentation. The idea was to have an actual takeoff of a liquid-fuel rocket on the day of the premiere. That could not be done, but the VfR acquired the "hardware" constructed for Oberth's experiments.

Early in the year 1930 a car was given a demonstration run, propelled by the liquid-fuel rocket that Valier and

* In the United States the film ran under the title *By Rocket to the Moon,* but sometimes under the title *The Girl in the Moon,* which is the translation of the German title.

Riedel had built in Dr. Heylandt's factory. Valier knew by that time that a test stand would be a superior means of developing a liquid-fuel rocket engine. But the public expected to see a moving vehicle. The car did perform, though the exhaust of the rocket was quite smoky, indicating poor combustion. Valier set to work to improve the rocket.

And later the engine exploded during a test run, almost instantly killing Max Valier, who had been standing next to it. The tragic date was May 17, 1930.

The men of the VfR learned two lessons. One was that they must use a firmly anchored test stand for their work. The other was that elaborate safety precautions were needed. One should observe a rocket motor burn from a distance, from "cover" in the military sense of the word. If possible, the observation should be indirect, by looking into a mirror. Of course, an automatic movie camera would have been fine, but there was no money for such refinements.

On September 27, the VfR established a proving ground, on the outskirts of Berlin.

The year 1931 brought real progress.

On March 14, almost precisely five years after the date of Goddard's first shot (which Goddard still kept secret), the first European liquid-fuel rocket made its flight. Its designer was Johannes Winkler. It looked like nothing ever built before. There were three pipes, arranged like an equilateral triangle. One of the pipes held liquid methane gas ($CH_4$), the second liquid oxygen, and the third compressed nitrogen for pressurizing the other two. Sheet metal held the tanks in position. When lying on its side, Winkler's rocket looked somewhat like a triangular box kite. The rocket motor was near the top, pointing downward, located in the center of the triangle. Weird, but it worked.

On April 11, Dr. Heylandt's chief engineer, Joachim

Pietsch, made a demonstration run of the car that Valier had built. The rocket motor worked better this time, but it still was not perfect.

On May 14, 1931, the first rocket of the VfR climbed into the sky. It consisted of two pipes for tanks, one for liquid oxygen and one for gasoline. The oxygen built up its own pressure by partially evaporating in the uninsulated tank. Pressure for the gasoline was supplied by compressed carbon dioxide. The two pipes were held together by struts. The struts at the upper end also held the rocket motor in place, and the struts at the lower end held tail fins in place. Later on, they also carried a container for a small parachute.

What had Dr. Goddard and Tsander's group been doing in the meantime?

Well, Prof. Goddard had moved from New England to New Mexico in October 1930 and set up shop on the Mescalero Ranch near Roswell. He worked mainly on rocket-motor development and began experiments dealing with the stabilization of a rocket's flight by means of gyroscopes.*

Tsander's first rocket, called OR-1, had been completed in 1930, but nobody knows whether it was tested. Quite possibly, Tsander considered it just as an exercise in rocket engineering; other experimenters have done the same. By the time OR-2 was ready for testing, Tsander was in a hospital near Kislovodsk in the Caucasus mountains. The test was run by members of the Mosgird in March 1933, just in time to inform Tsander that it had worked well. He died ten days after the test. These tests did not involve takeoffs. The first Russian rocket to fly was called ORM-50; it had been finished by Mihail Konstantinovitch Tikhonravov,

* He returned to Clark University, Worcester, Massachusetts, in 1932 and went back to New Mexico in September 1934. His main experiments were not to take place before 1934.

who also conducted the flight test on August 17, 1933. The rocket had a takeoff weight of only 22 pounds and was about 8 feet tall. Tikhonravov later said that it had worked well, but never revealed how high it reached. Tikhonravov then proceeded to build the second Russian rocket, which made its flight on November 25, 1933.

Since there is no private enterprise in the Soviet Union— except on a very small scale—these rocket tests must be considered government activity. By 1932 German rocket research had turned into a government activity, too. A few years earlier, the scientists in the Weapons Office of the German army had wondered whether rockets in new form could not become military weapons again, as gunpowder rockets had been at the time of the Napoleonic wars. An officer was assigned to look around and to find out whether a university or an industrial firm could not be persuaded to do research. The universities declined, and industry was not interested. Presumably the contracts offered were too small.

Another officer was then put in charge; his name was Walter Dornberger, his rank was captain, and he held a doctorate in engineering. Dornberger informed himself about what had been done. He received an emphatic "no" from Dr. Heylandt, who wanted absolutely nothing to do with rockets because of Valier's death. He came to the VfR's proving ground—not in uniform, of course—and decided that an army subsidy to the VfR would never be kept secret. He finally went to his superiors and told them that the army, if it wanted rockets, had to do its own development work. After some debate, his plan of starting a subsection of the Weapons Office for rocket development was approved. It was to be located at Kummersdorf West, which was an artillery proving ground about an hour's drive from the center of Berlin. And then he hired a young member of the VfR who had caught his eye: Wernher von Braun.

This was the beginning of modern rocketry. The funds of the Weapons Office were not unlimited; in fact, they were small, but it was more money than other rocket experimenters had ever seen at one time. And it was a great advantage that the section chief was an engineer himself. By the end of 1932 the rocket research group of the Weapons Office consisted of four people: Dr. Dornberger (meanwhile promoted to colonel); Wernher von Braun, who had not yet received his doctorate; Heinrich Grünow, a highly trained mechanic; and Walter J. H. Riedel, who had been an employee of Dr. Heylandt.

By 1933 they produced their first rocket, called Aggregate-1 or A-1 for short. Its rocket motor produced a thrust of 650 pounds, and the whole rocket weighed about half that. But A-1 never made a test flight. Another rocket, called A-2 was designed, and two specimens were taken to the island of Borkum in the North Sea. They made their flights in December 1934, reaching altitudes of about 6500 feet.

By the end of 1934 this was the high-altitude record for liquid-fuel rockets, but one year later it was no longer the record. On March 28, 1935, a Goddard rocket climbed to 4800 feet, and on May 31 another Goddard rocket reached 7500 feet. During the same year the Russians made about a dozen shots which did not become known then. The highest went to six miles.

Early in 1936 six different groups, large and small, were actively working on liquid-fuel rockets: (1) the Moscow group under Tikhonravov, (2) the German army group in Kummersdorf, busy with something called A-3, (3) Dr. Eugen Sänger, an Austrian by birth, working for the German Luftwaffe with the ultimate goal of rocket-propelled

**33**

interceptor aircraft, (4) Robert Esnault-Pelterie, trying to create a high-altitude research rocket, (5) the American Rocket Society in the New York area, striving for an efficient liquid-fuel rocket motor, and (6) Professor Robert H. Goddard in New Mexico, with the same ultimate goal as REP.

Late in 1940 the number had shrunk to two, the Kummersdorf group and Sänger. The Russians had been put to work on something else, presumably more conventional military weapons. The others had just dropped out, REP because of an accident, the ARS mainly because of lack of permanent facilities, and Professor Goddard for lack of financial support.

During those four years the German army group made all the progress there was. In 1937 the rocket men left Kummersdorf and went to Peenemünde on the large island of Usedom. They now had the Baltic Sea as a firing range. Their first shots there were three A-3 rockets, which were very large by the then prevailing standard, standing over 21 feet tall with a diameter of 2 feet 3½ inches and a takeoff weight of 1650 pounds. These three shots were not successful; the rocket motors worked fine, but nothing else did. A better A-3 had to be created before they could go on, but they called the improved A-3 by the designation A-5 to avoid the bad reputation of the A-3. A-5 did work well, and they could now go on to the design of A-4, which was to become known to history as V-2.

The final version of this rocket, which was used to bombard England in the last year of the Second World War, stood 47 feet tall, had a diameter of 5 feet 5 inches, carried a warhead weighing 2205 pounds, and had a takeoff weight of 28,229 pounds. Of this weight 19,392 pounds were fuel (liquid oxygen and alcohol); the rest was the warhead and the structure of the rocket. It could reach a target 190 miles from the firing site. It was never purposely left on the vertical path which it followed during the first ten seconds after lift-off. However, a few times the mechanism that tilted the rocket in the direction of the target failed to work, and then altitudes of about 100 miles were attained.

The wartime missile could be used, without any other change than removal of the warhead, to be what Robert Esnault-Pelterie and Robert H. Goddard had tried to build: an instrument carrier for the exploration of the upper atmosphere.

The first A-4 rocket that was completed at Peenemünde was left alone; it was something to show to official visitors who might drop in. The second and the third misbehaved, but the fourth, fired on October 3, 1942, worked perfectly. Dornberger and Oberth shook hands and said, "Today the spaceship has been invented." The range of the fourth A-4 was 118 miles, somewhat shorter than expected because the trajectory had been a little too steep.

About a dozen failures followed after this first success, but finally the rocket could be considered a workable device. Over 2000 of them were fired as weapons, and by January 1, 1945, the whole world knew that the Germans had the biggest rocket ever. If people in other countries wondered how this could have happened, it only proved that they did not know even an outline of rocket history. If a group of competent scientists and engineers, well organized and having sufficient funds, works without any competition whatever for four years, it is not at all surprising that they can do much better than their early competitors who had to give up for one reason or another.

# CHAPTER III

# The New Beginning:
# Reaching Space

WHEN the Second World War drew to its close
during the early months of 1945, the Allies were not only
fighting for a military victory, they also were after German
secrets.

One of these secrets was the German atomic energy
project, which was hotly pursued by American intelligence
teams. They pressed the search relentlessly, first interview-
ing Italian scientists about it after the Allies had driven the
Germans out of Italy. Then they did the same to French
scientists after France had been liberated. The intelligence
teams drew blanks everywhere; they even berated Italian
scientists for being still "loyal" to the Germans by guarding
their secrets. Only after Germany itself had been occupied
did the intelligence teams begin to realize, slowly and reluc-
tantly, that the Nazi government simply had not paid any
attention to atomic energy. It was estimated later that the
United States spent more money trying to find the German
"atomic energy project" than the Germans had spent on
atomic research.

The other "secret" urgently traced was the rocket called V-2. Actually it was not much of a secret any more, because one of these rockets had crashed in Sweden. It had not carried a warhead—the purpose of that particular shot had been to test the guidance mechanism of another rocket—so it had not exploded on impact. It was smashed up, but not so badly that it could not be reconstructed. The construction of the rocket was known, therefore, but the Allies wanted undamaged specimens and the story behind the development of this rocket.

In this search the American teams were very lucky.

The German research and planning staff had fled Peenemünde when the Red Army approached and had been in hiding for a brief period in Bavaria. They voluntarily surrendered under the leadership of Dr. Wernher von Braun, who had trouble making the Americans believe that he was indeed the leader of the team. To the Americans he looked "too young and too jolly" to have such an important position.

Another American group had located the place where the V-2 rockets were manufactured, the so-called *Mittelwerk* near the town of Niedersachswerfen in the Harz mountains. All the finished and unfinished parts of the rockets were removed and shipped to the United States. It was necessary to manufacture some parts that were in short supply, but the parts from the Mittelwerk, augmented by American-made parts, resulted in a total of 75 rockets, of which 68 were in working order.

The British succeeded in finding two undamaged specimens of the rocket; most of those located in the field had been disabled by retreating German troops by firing machine gun bullets into them. The two undamaged rockets were shipped to the seaport of Cuxhaven and fixed by German crews under British supervision into the North Sea.

The Russians also captured two undamaged rockets which had been in Poland, where they were to be used for the training of firing crews. The Russians shipped the rockets and the training and service manuals to Russia, where they set up a production line for making V-2 rockets. Translating the manuals was easy, and copying the rockets was fairly easy, too, but the Russians knew that the actual firing was a question of practice and for practice they needed more than the two rockets they had captured. Just how many they made is not known; estimates range from 400 to 800 rockets. Witnesses could tell later that rocket firings went on day and night over a period of weeks.

That done, the Russians went on to their own designs, the first of which, called *Pobyeda* (Victory) seems to have been a V-2 with much longer fuel tanks. But the next type after that was purely a Russian design.

A dozen years ago one could read in many places that the Russian rockets were built for them by captured German scientists. Readers accepted these stories as a convenient explanation of the Russian successes, but it simply was not true. The Russians, annoyed by the fact that the German research and planning staff had surrendered to the Americans, took about two hundred men and their families from the Mittelwerk to Russia. As long as the Russians fired copies of the German rocket, some of these men were kept on the proving ground to answer questions as they came up. But as soon as Russian designs were being tested, non-Russians were no longer permitted on the proving grounds. The German engineers sat in reasonable comfort on an island in a Russian lake, received questions about production problems in writing, and had to answer the questions in writing. After about four years they were sent home.

Of course, one can say that the Germans helped the Russians by way of example: they had shown that large rockets could be built and that still larger ones should be possible. But that example went for all countries, not only for the Soviet Union. The point is that the Germans, by having jumped ahead of everybody, provided a new beginning for rocket research. Everybody could now begin with the V-2 as the foundation for advanced rocket research.

This went for the French as well as for the British, who had not done much along that line. It also went for the Russians, who realized that everything they had done before 1940 was now hopelessly obsolete. It also went for the United States, but to a somewhat lesser extent, for the United States had not been completely idle.

Goddard, as has been told, left the Mescalero Ranch in October 1940 because he could not obtain financial support from the Guggenheim Foundation any longer. After Pearl Harbor he offered his services to the Navy, and the Navy, after deliberating on what might be needed, put him to work on rocket motors that were to assist the takeoff of amphibious planes. Professor Hugo Junkers had released enough information about his own experiments a dozen years earlier to indicate that it was a promising method. The U.S. Army Air Corps knew about it, too, of course, but they felt that they could always build sufficiently long runways for land-based airplanes. The Navy had the problem of comparatively short runways on aircraft carriers or of takeoff from water, which is always more difficult than takeoff from a runway, so the Navy welcomed rocket-assisted takeoff. In order to get results fast, three different groups were put to work on such units. The so-called JATO (Jet-Assisted TakeOff; in spite of the name, these units were rockets, not jets in our sense which had not then been invented) units of the California group were the ones actually used.

His work on rocket units for the Navy was the last piece

of research Goddard did. In 1945 he developed cancer of the larynx and died on August 10 of that year.

The California group, which eventually grew into the Aerojet Company (later re-named Aerojet General Corporation), had started out as a group of graduate students of the California Institute of Technology, advised by Hungarian-born Professor Theodor von Kármán. The goal of the group that had formed in 1936 was the creation of a high-altitude instrument-carrying research rocket. But it was a long time before they could pursue this goal. First they developed an entirely new kind of solid fuels, called the GALCIT fuels, which were used in the JATO units mentioned. The letters of the name stand for Guggenheim Aeronautical Laboratory, California Institute of Technology.

In November 1943 Professor von Kármán sent a letter about the long-neglected high-altitude rocket to the Ordnance Department; the letter was also signed by Dr. Frank J. Malina and Dr. Hsue-shen Tsien. Within two months the Ordnance Department agreed, and Project ORDCIT (ORDnance and California Institute of Technology) was underway. The first rocket of the project, a solid-fuel rocket, was named Private A and tested in December 1944 near Barstow, California. The second rocket was called Private F; it also was a solid-fuel rocket, and it was tested in April 1945 at Fort Bliss, Texas.

Having gathered experience with these solid-fuel rockets, the researchers felt that they were ready for the real job, and they designed a liquid-fuel high-altitude rocket with a solid-fuel booster which consisted of a cluster of battlefield rockets that were known to be both powerful and reliable. The rocket was named WAC-Corporal, and the dimensions (without the booster) were: 16 feet tall, 1 foot in diameter, overall weight with fuel 665 pounds. The rocket motor produced a thrust of 1500 pounds. The rocket was ready in the summer of 1945 and was shipped for testing to a place that had changed its status only recently.

While the V-2 parts from the Mittelwerk were made ready for shipment to the United States, a group of officers from Ordnance and Military Engineers were looking for a place that could be made into a large proving ground. The site finally chosen was only 60 miles from the Mescalero Ranch. It was a flat valley due north of El Paso, Texas, located in New Mexico. Since the White Sands National Monument is in the same valley, the proving ground was called the White Sands Proving Ground. The WAC-Corporal was fired from there during September and October 1945 and reached an altitude of 43.5 miles.

By that time the V-2 parts also were at the White Sands Proving Ground, and Dr. von Braun and his men were housed in nearby Fort Bliss. A careful program called logically the V-2 Program had been worked out. The V-2s were to be fired at the rate of about two a month for scientific purposes. At the same time, the firings would acquaint American engineers and military personnel with the handling and firing of large rockets.

The first test of a V-2 at White Sands took place on March 15, 1946, but it was not a flight. It was a static test on a test stand built into the side of a mountain. The first flight test took place on April 16, 1946, and it was not a success; the rocket rose to only 5 miles. But the next try, on May 10, was successful; the V-2 climbed to 70 miles. The sixth flight after the first success, made on July 30, resulted in a peak altitude of 104 miles. Two other rockets reached the same altitude; two more went even higher, to 116 and 128 miles.

Not all the V-2 rockets were used in the scientific program. A few were used for special tests; one was a takeoff from an aircraft carrier, another was called Operation Pushover. The name meant just what it said: a fully fueled rocket was made to fall on a simulated ship's deck, constructed for this purpose on dry land to see how much damage would be caused if a rocket fell over accidentally. The damage was considerable, though details have not been released. And eight rockets were used in Project Bumper.

Project Bumper was a marriage of the V-2 and the WAC-Corporal, meaning that the WAC-Corporal was used as an upper stage for a V-2. The V-2 could have carried a rocket three times as heavy as the WAC-Corporal, but no such rocket was then available. The first shot of Project Bumper was fired on February 24, 1949. At an altitude of about 20 miles the V-2 had exhausted its fuel and the two rockets were separated so that the WAC-Corporal could go on under its own power. The empty V-2 continued to climb to 70 miles before it started to fall back. While it was doing that, the WAC-Corporal coasted to a peak altitude of 250 miles. It was the first time a rocket penetrated into space far above the atmosphere.

No higher shot was made for a number of years. There was no need to go higher. The next step would be not to go higher, but to go into orbit.

But it should be noted that the Navy's Viking rocket established a high-altitude record for single-stage liquid-fuel rockets five years later. Viking-XI, fired on May 24, 1954, climbed to 158 miles.

It would be interesting to know how far, or how high, the Russians had gone at that time.

Now—before we can go on with the story of Sputnik and other triumphs—we have to learn a little more about satellites.

Tsiolkovsky had talked about putting a spaceship into orbit around the earth in his second publication. Hermann

Oberth had advocated the same in his book published in 1923. During the year 1928 the monthly journal of the VfR had carried articles by Guido von Pirquet dealing with a triple space station, one in orbit not too high above the atmosphere, another one in orbit several thousand miles out, and a third one in an eccentric orbit touching the orbits of the other two for the easy transfer of men and material from the inner station to the outer station or the other way around.

And in 1929 a whole book on the manned space station had appeared, written by an Austrian army captain in the engineer corps by the name of Potočnik; he wrote under the pen name of Hermann Noordung. Potočnik-Noordung also spoke about three space stations, but he wanted them in the synchronous orbit and close together. One was to be a power plant, converting solar energy into electric current; the second was to be an astronomical observatory; while the third was to be a wheel-shaped structure where the people would live during the periods they were not on duty.

All four of them had talked in terms of manned space stations. Neither they, nor anybody else, had ever even conceived of an unmanned satellite of relatively small size that could be controlled by radio instead of by men.

To understand this lack of foresight one only has to look at the dates of publication of these books and articles. They were all printed before 1930, and at that time another branch of engineering, radio and electronics, was very young. Radio still had to grow up, though the radio engineers of that period probably thought that they had already grown up.

It is an interesting fact that the early products of a new branch of engineering are usually large in size, heavy in weight, and clumsy in construction. The British engineers of a century and a half ago who wanted to build railroads with steam locomotives were told that it could not be done. Nobody doubted that railroads could be built; in fact, a few short tracks with horse-drawn railroad cars were in existence. But the idea of using a steam engine to pull these cars was sheer nonsense. Steam engines were things that were used to pump water from mine shafts, and they were housed in separate buildings in the main area. How could anybody dream of putting such a monster on rails?

The problem, of course, was to build a small steam engine.

At the beginning of the present century, the same story was repeated with aviation and the internal-combustion engine. An engine that produced 30 horsepower was a magnificent thing, but it was nearly the size of a small car of today with an 80-horsepower engine hidden somewhere under the hood. In 1910 a German research engineer wrote a well-reasoned article on the future of aviation. In this article he pointed out that big airships like those built by Count Ferdinand von Zeppelin did not have much of a problem. They had enough capacity to carry several heavy engines. But the airplane would stay just an interesting toy until a lightweight engine could be built. The author of that article then went on to say that an airplane, to be reliable, would need a 75-horsepower engine and that engine must not weigh more than 1 kilogram (equal to 2.2 pounds) per horsepower. Probably thinking of the story of the steam engine (which, in the case of ships' engines, had not lost weight but had become far more powerful for the same weight), he did not doubt that an airplane engine weighing only 170 pounds and delivering 75 horsepower would eventually be built. But, he concluded, it would not be soon.

In the period from 1920 to 1930 radio went through the same evolution. A radio receiver for the home was a piece of furniture, not something one could tuck away on the book shelf. And a broadcasting station, especially one for business use, instead of for entertainment broadcasting, was something incredible. In 1925 I was taken on a guided tour of the German "overseas radio station" at Nauen near Berlin, which mainly sent telegrams to the United States and South America. There were half a dozen major and about sixteen minor antenna towers. The total antenna length was 17,000 meters (56,000 feet), and there were several buildings housing the generators for the broadcasting power needed. Each transmitter would have taken up all the space in a modern trailer truck.

Nobody could, or would, dream of putting a radio station into orbit.

Without a radio transmitter the tracking of a satellite is a difficult job that can be done by only a few installations. The other function of the transmitter is to relay instrument readings to the ground stations.

Instruments that could detect such items as air pressure and temperature and record them on a strip of paper did exist, though they were clumsy, too. What good was a set of instruments in orbit if one could not get their records to the ground to be read? The method of making such instruments report their readings over a distance—now called telemetry—had been invented before the First World War. But it was done over a telegraph wire, radio not being considered reliable enough. It was theoretically possible to do it by radio, but the means had not been worked out.

Nobody considered unmanned artificial satellites, or even radio contact from manned satellites. Quite a number of things had to happen before an unmanned artificial satellite could be thought about. Rockets had to grow much bigger and more powerful in order to reach beyond the atmosphere. Instruments measuring temperature, air pressure, etc., had to evolve into much smaller and lighter versions, which also

**45**

had to be more sensitive and respond faster.* Most important: radio transmitters had to lose both weight and bulk, in order to get such information back to earth.

By 1946 all these developments had taken place. Rockets had grown large, at first for military purposes. Instruments no longer had moving parts which were comparatively heavy and also slow, but worked with electronic tubes and, still later, with transistors. And transmitters had acquired a reasonable size and weight. Other useful inventions had also been made in the meantime—small and fast automatic switches and, last but by no means least, recording tape. With all these things in existence, one could think of useful unmanned satellites.

Three British engineers, K. W. Gatland, A. M. Kunesch, and A. E. Dixon, thought about small satellites in preparation for the Second International Congress on Astronautics, held in London in 1951. But of the seventeen papers presented during that Congress fourteen discussed various problems connected with manned space stations, two dealt with the problem of returning from a satellite orbit to the ground, and only the one by Gatland, Kunesch, and Dixon talked about unmanned satellites.

It contained four suggestions, called schemes A, B, C, and D. For all four schemes, the orbit was supposed to be a circular one 500 miles above sea level, and the assumed rockets were all three-stage rockets.

Scheme A had the purpose of just getting *something* into orbit to see how stable an object would be in an orbit com-

---

* The term "response" or "time-lag" means the time between a change and the time when the instrument actually indicates the change. Imagine that a thermometer is moved very rapidly from a room where the temperature is 80° F. to another room where it is only 50° F. The time the thermometer needs to go down to 50° F. is the time-lag.

**46**

paratively close to the earth. The "something" would be the third stage which, after it had burned all its fuel, would weigh 155 pounds. The three-stage rocket needed to accomplish that would have a takeoff weight of 37,000 pounds, or 8,700 pounds more than the V-2. It was suggested that the third stage should have no control equipment of any kind; to save weight, all the guidance and control were to be in the second stage. This suggestion was followed six years later when the American Vanguard satellite carrier was designed, though I don't know whether the designers of Vanguard took the suggestion from that paper or thought of it themselves.

Scheme B was to put a satellite weighing 220 pounds into orbit; the empty third stage, weighing 770 pounds, would be orbited, too. But the rocket that could do that would have to have a takeoff weight of 137,300 pounds, which sounded monstrous at the time.

Scheme C was to orbit the same payload, but with an extra 165 pounds of guidance and control equipment in the rocket. For that, the takeoff weight would have to be an even 200,000 pounds.

For Scheme D the satellite weight was increased to 480 pounds, but the designers hoped that a new rocket design would make it possible to hold the takeoff weight down to the same figure as for Scheme C. The new design consisted of having the third stage inside the second stage and the second stage inside the first stage. The stages were, in effect, outer shells around inner shells, and the shells, being fuel tanks, were to be thrown off as soon as they were empty. So far, nobody has ever tried to build a rocket of that type. Probably the mechanical difficulties would be too great.

In 1953 Professor S. Fred Singer, then of the University of Maryland, had a complete design for an artificial satellite ready. It received the nickname MOUSE, for

Minimum Orbital Unmanned Satellite of Earth, and it was estimated that it would weigh a little over a hundred pounds. But in 1953 there was not yet a rocket that could carry a hundred pounds into orbit.

Before going on with satellites, we have to turn to the subject of orbiting.

# CHAPTER IV

# The Orbit of a Satellite

WHEN, during the early part of October 1957, Russia's Sputnik I beeped its way around the earth, the public had to learn a number of facts—and words—which seemed to be brand-new. There was this device named *Sputnik*; it was in *orbit* around the earth; it was 142 miles above sea level when it went through the *perigee* of its orbit; it was 588 miles above sea level when it went through the *apogee* of its orbit; and its *orbital period* was 96 minutes.

All new words, the public thought.

In reality, it was all old-hat to astronomers.

The only one of these words that could be called new was the word "sputnik" itself, but only because it was Russian. In Russia the term was old-hat, too. It was, in a sense, even old-fashioned, dating from the time when people walked from village to village. The word meant somebody who happened to walk with you, or ride in some horse-drawn vehicle, in the same direction on the road. The Russian word for road is *put* (pronounced *poot*) and a sputnik (*s*, in Russian, means "with") was simply a "road companion."

Russian astronomers, in the time before the First World

War, began to use this old term in their own science. The planet Jupiter has four large moons, two of them about the same size as our own moon and two of them larger than our moon. But Jupiter also has a number of much smaller moons. While the four large moons are respectable moons, the small ones were half-jokingly called *sputniki* by the Russians—just road companions of Jupiter on his path around the sun.

It was only logical that Tsiolkovsky, when he thought about artificial satellites of earth, called them by the same word. And the Russian scientists and engineers who prepared the first Russian artificial satellite for launching also used the word. To them it was not a name, it was just a handy term that happened to be around.

But how about those other words, like orbit, perigee, apogee, and so forth? They were even older, having been invented by the German astronomer Johannes Kepler back in 1608, just before the invention of the telescope. The Danish astronomer Tycho Brahe, who had died in 1601, had left to Kepler many hundreds of notes on his observations of the planet Mars. These were not "observations" as we understand the term. To us an observation of a planet means a drawing of what can be seen through a telescope. In Tycho Brahe's time there were no telescopes; for this reason, his observations referred to the position of Mars in the sky, relative to the fixed stars. Tycho Brahe, an irascible man in daily life, was very careful when it came to observing the planets and the stars. He did not mind doing the same observation over and over again; he wanted to be sure that what he set down on paper was correct. Moreover, he had excellent eyesight. In short, Kepler could trust a slip of paper on which Brahe had written where Mars had been in the sky at a certain time on a certain night.

Kepler, in working his way through Tycho Brahe's notes,

had a purpose in mind—he wanted to find out what the shape of the orbit of Mars is. An older idea that was around at the time was that the orbit of a celestial body had to be a circle, or a combination of two circles of different sizes. Kepler was convinced that Mars moved around the sun. But the idea of a circular orbit did not go with Tycho Brahe's observations. In other words, Mars, if it moved in the supposed circular orbit, could not have been seen in the sky where it had been seen.

Therefore the orbit of Mars had to have another shape. But what was it? For a while Kepler thought that it might be an oval, that is, egg-shaped, with one end more pointed than the other. That did not work, either. Suddenly, while looking at his calculations, he realized that the orbit was probably an ellipse. He made a few other calculations and found that Tycho Brahe's observations agreed with an elliptical orbit.

An ellipse has a faint resemblance to an egg shape, but both ends have the same degree of roundness. But while an ellipse has, of course, a center, the sun is not at the center of an elliptical orbit, but in the place called the focus, or focal point, by mathematicians. Or rather, it is in one of the focal points, since an ellipse has two of them. The other focal point is empty.

Having found that the orbit of a planet around the sun is an ellipse, Kepler also realized that a few new words were needed. The word "orbit" was of Latin origin—the Romans used the term *orbita* when they spoke of the ruts made by wagon wheels in a country road. In Kepler's elliptical orbits there evidently was a point where the planet was closest to the sun. This point Kepler called perihelion, from *Helios*, the Greek name of the sun god, and from *peri*, which means "to go around." There also had to be a point in the orbit where the planet was farthest from the sun. Kepler used

51

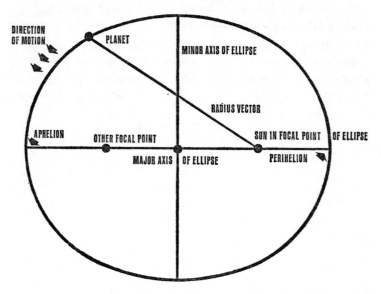

Fig. 3. An elliptical orbit, showing the locations of the focal points. The eccentricity of this orbit has been exaggerated to show the relationships clearly. No major planet has such an orbit, but many comets have.

the Greek word *apo* (to go, or to be, away) and the name of that point became apohelion, later shortened to aphelion.

If the orbit had been a circle with the sun in the center, the line from the sun to the planet would be a radius. But since the orbit was an ellipse, and the sun was not in the center, a line from the sun to the planet in a given position needed another name. Kepler called it *radius vector*.

For the orbit of the moon around the earth the terms had to be changed a bit. Instead of the name of the sun god Helios, the Greek word for the earth, *gaia*, was used, contracted to *gee*. Hence *perigee* for the point nearest the earth and *apogee* for the point farthest away.

There is an important difference between the apogee

of our natural moon and the apogee of an artificial satellite. When it is stated that the distance between the earth and the moon at apogee is 252,000 miles, this means the distance from the center of the earth to the center of the moon. But when the distance of an artificial satellite is mentioned, it is the distance of the satellite from sea level.

There are two reasons for making this distinction. The first is that it is easier to visualize. When you hear that a satellite is passing 800 miles overhead you think in terms of the observer; the satellite is 800 miles from his eyes. Of course, the distance from the center of the earth must be used when the orbit is to be calculated; but to tell somebody that a satellite in a nearly circular orbit is 4,760 miles away only means that he has to subtract 3,960 miles (the radius of the earth) in order to find out that the satellite is 800 miles above him. The other reason why the orbits of artificial satellites are given as distances from sea level is to stresss the fact that they are artificial and not natural.

Next we come to the shape of a satellite's orbit. It is, strictly speaking, always an ellipse. That closed orbits are elliptical is called Kepler's First Law. But some artificial satellites have been placed into orbits that differ so little from a circle that they, for practical purposes, can be called circular orbits. A short list of such circular orbits shows that the orbital period, the time required to complete one orbit, grows the longer the farther the satellite is from the earth. Here is such a list.

| Distance from sea level (miles) | Orbital period | Velocity in Orbit (mi. per sec.) |
|---|---|---|
| 346 | 96 min. | 4.69 |
| 470 | 105 min. | 4.41 |
| 1075 | 120 min. | 4.39 |
| 3200 | 3½ hrs. | 3.58 |
| 4000 | 4 hrs. | 3.47 |
| 7700 | 7 hrs. | 2.90 |

That a satellite 4000 miles away needs longer to complete an orbit than a satellite 470 miles away will surprise no one; the 4000-mile orbit is obviously much longer. But many people are surprised to learn that the rate of motion is slower the farther the orbit. The answer is relatively simple. The forward motion of the satellite must be fast enough to compensate for the "downward" motion produced by the earth's gravitational attraction. At a greater distance from the earth the gravitational attraction is weaker, and a slower motion will compensate for the weaker gravity.

It is also necessary to understand what is called the "inclination." Again, this is originally an astronomical term. You can read in a book on astronomy that the orbit of Mars has an inclination of 1 degree and 51 minutes of arc. This means that the orbits of Mars and of the earth, seen edge on, look like Fig. 4. The orbit of the earth is considered as zero.

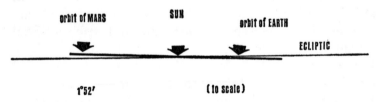

Fig. 4. The orbits of the earth and of Mars, seen on edge to show the inclination.

Usually one does not speak of the orbit of earth in this connection, but of the plane of the earth's orbit, which has the name "ecliptic." The difference between the earth's orbit and the ecliptic can be best understood if one imagines a very large sheet of stiff paper with a fairly small circle drawn in its center. The drawn circle is the orbit of earth;

54

the surface of the sheet of stiff paper is the ecliptic. In the case of all other planets and all comets and even our own moon, the inclination is always the angle formed by the orbit of the other body with the ecliptic.

But in the case of artificial satellites the figure for the inclination is the angle between the satellite orbit and the earth's equator. Most of the time nobody is interested in the angle formed by the satellite orbit and the ecliptic—it is the equator that counts. If a satellite stays over the equator all the way around, its inclination is zero; if a satellite goes over both poles, its inclination is 90 degrees of arc.

If a satellite has an inclination of 30 degrees of arc—most of the satellites fired from Cape Kennedy have about that inclination—it will be vertically overhead during each orbit both 30 degrees north of the equator and 30 degrees south of the equator. In general, the Russian satellites show much higher inclinations than the American satellites, because they are fired from points farther north than Cape Kennedy. If you fire a satellite due east from Philadelphia, its inclination would be 40 degrees of arc, because Philadelphia is on the 40th parallel north of the equator. If you fired a satellite from Valdivia in Chile, the inclination would also be 40 degrees of arc because Valdivia is very nearly on the 40th parallel to the south of the equator.

Of course, one could put a satellite into an orbit with an inclination of 60 degrees from Cape Kennedy. The trick involved is as simple as possible; one would not fire the rocket into a straight easterly direction after takeoff, but fire it in a northeasterly direction. And if the top stage of the carrier rocket can be re-ignited after orbit has been reached, the inclination of the orbit can be changed. But there is rarely a reason for doing this.

Since the normal orbit of a satellite goes east from the

takeoff point, the satellite travels in the same direction in which the earth turns. However, as it travels much faster than the earth turns, it will overtake all points on the ground. For this reason artificial satellites "rise" in the west and "set" in the east. Those with orbits of high inclination will "rise" in the southwest and "set" in the northeast. But there are some satellites that are 60,000 miles away; if one could watch them, one would find that they "rise" in the east and "set" in the west. Beyond a certain distance out, the satellite begins to travel slower than the earth turns.

That distance is 22,300 miles from sea level, and the satellites that orbit at that distance (there are several) neither rise nor set. The orbit at that distance has been named the "synchronous orbit," because a satellite out there needs as much time to complete one orbit as the earth needs to turn on its axis. The orbital velocity in that orbit is 1.9 miles per second. These satellites that neither rise nor set can only be seen from a rather large area beneath them. From other areas they can never be seen.

Because satellites in orbits smaller than the synchronous orbit overtake places on the ground and satellites in the synchronous orbit keep pace with points on the ground, it follows that satellites in still larger orbits will "fall behind." These satellites will rise in the east and set in the west.

A satellite that orbits the earth at a distance of, say, 3000 miles will never leave its orbit. The gravitational influence of our natural moon will not influence it to an extent that could be detected, and the earth's atmosphere—which would brake its motion—is far below. Hence it is in a "permanent orbit." There are a number of satellites in such permanent orbits, but fortunately most satellites were in orbits that were not permanent. If every satellite had gone into a permanent orbit, nearby space would be so cluttered by now that manned space flight might be hazardous.* But hundreds of satellites that were in orbit during the last twelve years—some of them for only a week, others for a year or more—have returned to earth.

Their orbits had been elliptical, as is the rule, but it would be wrong to conclude that every satellite in an elliptical orbit must eventually re-enter the atmosphere and burn up. An elliptical orbit can also be permanent, provided only that its perigee is far above the atmosphere.

The motion of a satellite in an elliptical orbit can best be compared to the motion of a pendulum. The pendulum, "falling" from a certain height, does not come to rest at the lowest point of its swing, as one might expect if one didn't know better from experience. Instead of coming to a rest, it overshoots and climbs to the other side.

Similarly, a satellite that has reached its perigee does not stay at that lowest altitude of its orbit. After passing perigee, it climbs away from the earth again at a slant, losing velocity while so doing. At apogee it is slowest; then it approaches the earth again (slantwise) and gains velocity in the process, so that it is fastest at perigee.

A pendulum on earth will gradually slow down because of friction in the bearing and because of the resistance to its motion by the air. A satellite in an elliptical orbit will not slow down, unless its orbit touches the upper atmosphere at the perigee. If it does, the satellite will lose a little of its kinetic energy to air resistance, and the result is that the next apogee point is a little nearer to the ground than was the previous apogee point. In other words, its

* Only one collision between satellites is known to have occurred, and that collision was not serious. Two American satellites with very long antennas touched antennas on one occasion. It only had the result that both started spinning on their axes.

orbit grows gradually smaller * because the apogee comes closer and closer to the planet. The perigee remains roughly at the same altitude.

Finally, the whole orbit has shrunk to perigee altitude, which means that there is air resistance all the way around. Then the orbit changes once more; it now becomes a tight spiral that leads into lower and lower layers of the atmosphere. When sufficiently dense layers have been reached, the re-entry heat consumes the satellites; seen from the ground, these final moments of its existence look like a very bright meteor. The shrinkage of the orbit—technically known as "orbital decay"—is the reason why the number of satellites still in orbit is relatively small.

Only one more thing remains now to be discussed—the designation of a satellite. It so happens that most satellites have two designations. In the early days of American satellite-shooting, the Army put a number of satellites into orbits that did not have a high inclination. The first of them was called Explorer, and those that followed received the same name, followed by a number. That way the name became a designation; the term Explorer meant an American satellite with an orbit of low inclination.

Soon afterwards, the Air Force began putting satellites into near-polar orbits with a high inclination. They were all designated Discoverer. Several years later, satellites were put into orbit which had the purpose of watching the drift of air masses. They were designated Tiros, and everybody who knew the designations knew upon hearing the word Tiros that a weather-watch satellite was under discussion. The Russians designated their early satellites Sputnik, and later, when they orbited communications satellites, they called them *Molniya*, the Russian word for "lightning."

* For an example of a slowly shrinking orbit see the Appendix, where the shrinkage of the orbit of Explorer I is listed in detail.

These designations tell what the satellite does. They might be called national designations, because every nation makes up its own. In addition to the national designations there is an international designation, so to speak, for registration purposes. The American astronomer Fred L. Whipple made the first suggestion along these lines. He proposed that the first artificial satellite to achieve orbit during a calendar year (regardless of "nationality") be labeled 1958-alpha, the second 1958-beta, the third 1958-gamma, and so forth, using the letters of the Greek alphabet. Sometimes the satellite proper remains attached to the top stage of the carrier rocket, in which case only one orbiting object is produced. But more often the satellite is separated from the rocket so that one shot puts two objects into orbit. In that case the object that looks brighter (usually the carrier rocket, because it is bigger) would be called 1958-beta 1 and the other 1958-beta 2.

This proposal was adopted in 1958 and used until the end of 1962, except for one change made in 1959. The satellite trackers were not interested in brightness; they were interested in the satellites. Hence, beginning with the first satellite of 1959, the satellite always was number 1, the other orbiting objects then being numbered in order of size.

By the end of 1962 it could easily be predicted that there would be more satellites than there are letters in the Greek alphabet. Therefore, satellites were simply numbered and the number followed by the letter A, designating the satellite itself. The second Telstar communications satellite, orbited on the 7th of May 1963, became 1963 13A, and the orbiting top stage of its carrier rocket became 1963 13B. By the end of 1967 it turned out that more than one hundred satellites had been launched during the year and one more minor change had to be made. Beginning in January 1968, each satellite number had three digits: Russia's Kosmos-200, launched January 19, 1968, became 1968-006A. Near the end of that year four-digit numbers were introduced.

In many places in the United States huge blackish bubbles are stationed, clearly labeled U.S. SPACETRACK. What is visible is only the cover that protects the radar set and other instruments from bad weather. All these radars form a tracking network * which gathers the information of what is in orbit. This information goes to NASA's Goddard Space Flight Center in Greenbelt, Maryland.

There the Satellite Situation Report is issued every two weeks. Somebody who sees one of these reports for the first time and is intrigued by the title on the gray cardboard cover is due for a disappointment when he opens it.

Only a few names appear on each page, and an abbreviation of the country of origin; otherwise, there are figures, figures, figures.

However, figures are quite interesting if you know how to read them. Let us look at a few of the listings on that page and begin with 1968 0110A. This means, as has already been explained, the 110th artificial satellite orbited (by anybody) during 1968. The next item, 1968 0110B, is the orbiting top stage of the rocket.

The next column gives the name or designation of the satellite: OAO-A2. The letters OAO mean Orbiting Astronomical Observatory; the A2 indicates that it is the second of its kind. The first one, a few years earlier, unfortunately failed to work. Then comes the running catalogue number,

* Needless to say, the Russians have their own tracking stations, and the West European countries maintain ESTRAC, a third, though smaller, tracking network.

## OBJECTS IN ORBIT

| OBJECT | CODE NAME | CATALOGUE NUMBER | SOURCE | LAUNCH | PERIOD MINUTES | INCLI-NATION | APOGEE Km. | PERIGEE Km. | TRANSMITTING FREQ. (MC/S) |
|---|---|---|---|---|---|---|---|---|---|
| **1968 LAUNCHES (CONT'D)** | | | | | | | | | |
| 1968 0100D | | 3547 | US | 8 NOV | 97.8 | 32.8 | 932 | 372 | |
| 1968 0100E | | 3548 | US | 8 NOV | 97.8 | 32.8 | 932 | 372 | |
| 1968 0103A | PROTON 4 | 3544 | USSR | 16 NOV | 91.4 | 51.5 | 446 | 247 | |
| 1968 0103B | | 3545 | USSR | 16 NOV | 90.0 | 51.5 | 329 | 221 | |
| 1968 0106A | COSMOS 256 | 3576 | USSR | 30 NOV | 109.4 | 74.0 | 1226 | 1174 | |
| 1968 0106B | | 3577 | USSR | 30 NOV | 109.2 | 74.0 | 1222 | 1167 | |
| 1968 0107A | COSMOS 257 | 3578 | USSR | 3 DEC | 91.0 | 70.9 | 394 | 262 | |
| 1968 0107B | | 3579 | USSR | 3 DEC | 89.7 | 70.9 | 291 | 235 | |
| 1968 0109A | HEOS-A | 3595 | ESRO | 5 DEC | 6351.8 | 28.2 | 224436 | 439 | $136.650 |
| 1968 0110A | OAO-A2 | 3597 | US | 7 DEC | 100.3 | 34.9 | 776 | 766 | $136.441$136.259 $400.549 |
| 1968 0110B | | 3598 | US | 7 DEC | 100.2 | 34.9 | 813 | 720 | |
| 1968 0112B | | 3605 | US | 12 DEC | 114.4 | 80.3 | 1475 | 1387 | |
| 1968 0112C | | 3617 | US | 12 DEC | 114.0 | 80.1 | 1450 | 1380 | |
| 1968 0112D | | 3618 | US | 12 DEC | 114.7 | 80.5 | 1513 | 1379 | |
| 1968 0113A | COSMOS 259 | 3612 | USSR | 14 DEC | 99.3 | 48.4 | 1237 | 213 | $136.770$137.500 |
| 1968 0113B | | 3613 | USSR | 14 DEC | 99.0 | 48.4 | 1213 | 214 | |
| 1968 0113C | | 3614 | USSR | 14 DEC | 99.7 | 48.3 | 1274 | 213 | |
| 1968 0114A | ESSA 8 | 3615 | US | 15 DEC | 114.6 | 101.8 | 1465 | 1416 | |
| 1968 0114B | | 3616 | US | 15 DEC | 114.5 | 101.8 | 1461 | 1413 | |
| 1968 0115A | COSMOS 260 | 3619 | USSR | 16 DEC | 712.1 | 64.9 | 39589 | 489 | |
| 1968 0115B | | 3620 | USSR | 16 DEC | 91.2 | 65.0 | 435 | 235 | |
| 1968 0115C | | 3621 | USSR | 16 DEC | 90.2 | 64.9 | 355 | 218 | |
| 1968 0115D | | 3622 | USSR | 16 DEC | 708.4 | 64.8 | 39408 | 488 | |
| 1968 0116A | INTELSAT 3 F-2 | 3623 | US | 19 DEC | 1435.9 | 0.7 | 35810 | 35791 | |
| 1968 0117A | COSMOS 261 | 3624 | USSR | 19 DEC | 92.2 | 71.0 | 571 | 202 | |
| 1968 0117C-0117S$ | | | USSR | 19 DEC | HELIOCENTRIC ORBIT | | | | |
| 1968 0118B | | 3627 | US | 21 DEC | 95.0 | 48.4 | 780 | 257 | |
| 1968 0119A | COSMOS 262 | 3629 | USSR | 26 DEC | 94.8 | 48.4 | 767 | 257 | |
| 1968 0119B | | 3630 | USSR | 26 DEC | | | | | |

61

Fig. 5. A sample page from NASA's Satellite Situation Report. The page is p. 28 of vol. 9 #1.

3597 in this case. Everything in orbit, from a manned space-ship to a metal clamp that once held a satellite to a rocket, receives such a running number. Next is the country of origin, the United States in this case. (Sometimes the name of an organization is given, as in the item just above 0110A, where it says ESRO. The letters mean the European Space Research Organization.) Then comes the firing date. Then the orbital period: 100.3 minutes. The next column is the inclination of the satellite's orbit: 34.9 degrees of arc against the equator.

The next two columns give the apogee and the perigee of the orbit, the figures given in kilometers, partly because the metric system is the international system, partly because it is easier to calculate in the metric system. For the second OAO the figures are 766 kilometers (476.0 miles) for the perigee and 776 kilometers (482.2 miles) for the apogee. One can see at a glance that the orbit is almost a precise circle. The last column looks strangest: $136.441; $136.259; $400.549. This has nothing to do with prices or operating cost; the $ sign is used merely because the electrical print-out mechanism of the computer does not have the Greek letter *lambda* which indicates the wavelength of a trans-mission. The cryptic figures are just the frequencies used by OAO. The OAO can be ordered to transmit informa-tion at any time, because there is a storage battery in its circuits. If a satellite is powered directly by the sun and can, therefore, transmit only when it is in sunlight, the last column would read: & 136.290.

Let us examine two more items on that page of the Satel-lite Situation Report. 1968 0116A is INTELSAT 3, F-2, an international communications satellite. Its orbital period is listed as 1435.9 minutes; 1436 minutes is the time the earth needs to turn on its axis. This figure alone shows that this satellite belongs to the category of synchronous satellites, the satellites that keep pace with the earth's rotation and are neither slower nor faster. But even a synchronous satellite does not necessarily seem to hang motionlessly in one point of the sky. In order to do that it must orbit the earth over the equator. The listing shows that the inclination of INTELSAT 3 is 0.7 degrees of arc (a little more than the diameter of the full moon). The result of this inclination is that the satellite will move northward from the equator for six hours, spend the next six hours moving back to the equator, then move for six hours southward of the equator, and then return again. The figures for the perigee (35,791 kilometers) and for the apogee (35,810 kilometers) show that this orbit, too, is nearly a circle; the difference is only 19 kilometers, or 11.8 miles.

The next item, 1968 0117A, is the Russian satellite Kosmos-261, fired December 19. It has the typical orbit of a research satellite, with an orbital period of 92.2 minutes, a perigee at 202 kilometers (125.5 miles) and an apogee of 571 kilometers (354.8 miles). The item after 1968 0117A shows that this satellite shot produced 15 pieces of "space junk"; presumably there was some fuel left in the top stage of the carrier rocket which exploded.

Item 1968 0118B, with catalogue number 3627, is interesting for another reason. No orbital period or other figures are given. Instead, we find the notation "heliocentric orbit," meaning that this item is in orbit around the sun. The firing date (December 21) gives a clue about its nature. It is the third stage of the Saturn V rocket that sent Apollo 8 and its crew of three astronauts to the moon. The third stage, after it had done its duty, was maneuvered in such a way that it passed behind the moon and went into an orbit around the sun.

After a satellite has re-entered, it moves from the Objects in Orbit list of the Satellite Situation Report into the

Decayed Objects list, where the entry is short and simple. For example:

1967 104A Kosmos-185 3013 USSR 27 Oct. 14 Jan. 69

the first date being the launch date, the second date that of re-entry and burn-up in the atmosphere.

Artificial satellites either stay in orbit around the earth or else re-enter. For the whole of their lifetimes they move in the gravitational field of the earth only. But there are other types of space-going devices that leave the earth's gravitational field and move in the gravitational field of the moon or in that of the sun. Depending on their destinations, they are called lunar or planetary probes. The United States had three lunar programs: the Rangers, which were sent to crash on the moon, took pictures during the last 20 minutes of their flights; the Surveyors landed gently on the moon; and the Lunar Orbiters circled the moon. The Soviets launched 14 "Luna" probes. These programs and the planetary probes—the Mariner and the Zond—have been tabulated at the end of this book.

# CHAPTER V

# The Big Rockets

THE Redstone rocket, developed by Dr. Wernher von Braun and his team at the Redstone Arsenal near Huntsville, Alabama, was ready in 1953 but was classified as a military missile. Even the Redstone, then America's most powerful missile, was not powerful enough to reach satellite velocity by itself. No upper stages had been developed for it yet. And even with upper stages it could not have put a hundred-pound satellite into orbit. Rockets more powerful than the Redstone were still in the future. The Thor rocket of the Air Force made its first successful ballistic flights late in 1957; the still more powerful Atlas (also of the Air Force) made its first successful flights two months after the Thor. Neither was at the time used for a space shot.

Of course, nobody could know in 1953 when bigger rockets would be ready; hence all space thinking had to be based on the Redstone rocket, even though no information about the Redstone was released. Only the people who had built it knew what it could or could not do. The outcome of their thinking was that a 20-pound satellite might be orbited, using the Redstone as a booster and putting three

**65**

sets of solid-fuel Loki rockets on top of it. The topmost Loki rocket would carry some instruments and a small transmitter in its nose, and that top stage would be the artificial satellite.

It might be said right here that it was this arrangement that orbited the first American satellite, Explorer I, in 1958, but the Redstone rocket chosen for this shot had longer fuel tanks than the early model, the solid-fuel rockets on top were a later and more powerful version, and the burned-out top stage with its instrument section weighed about 38 pounds.

Four months earlier, the Russians had orbited their first artificial satellite, the famous Sputnik I and had proudly announced that its weight was 186 pounds. The launching of Sputnik proved that the Russians had rockets bigger and more powerful than either Redstone or Thor. This was an unpleasant surprise to both military men and politicians—but engineers and scientists could console themselves with one thought. That thought was: The Russians have proved that much larger rockets can be built, and if they could do it, we can do it, too.

The simplest way to compare one rocket with another is to compare the takeoff thrust. Dimensions do not mean very much. A rocket may be tall and thin, or it may be short and squat. Therefore it is meaningless to point out with pride that "our rocket is twenty feet taller than theirs." What counts is the power developed, expressed in pounds of thrust. Of course, the thrust of a rocket must be greater than its weight. If a rocket's weight were equal to its thrust, it would just hover over the launch pad.

The takeoff thrust of the Redstone was about 95,000 pounds. The takeoff thrust of the Russian rocket that put Sputnik I into orbit must have been about 600,000 pounds. The American Atlas rocket, still under development in

1957 and 1958 and a strict military secret, had a takeoff thrust of 360,000 pounds, which years later was increased to 380,000 pounds.

The Russians never permitted anybody to see the rocket that had put Sputnik 1 and Sputnik 2 into orbit. But many years later, in 1967, they displayed, at the Paris air show, the so-called Vostok rocket. That rocket must have been developed during the period from 1958 to 1960. Even when it was displayed in Paris, the Russians did not say how much thrust it developed, but from the array of rocket engines in its tail end, it was easy to estimate that the combined thrust must have been about 700,000 pounds.

The United States did not begin with the development of a more powerful rocket than the Atlas until 1962. The official position was that the Atlas was powerful enough for any job that might come up. It was said that the missions that had to be performed could be performed by the Atlas rocket, but this was done mainly by tailoring the missions in such a way that the Atlas could do them. All the time the fact remained that the American Atlas was only half as powerful as the Russian Vostok rocket.

Of course, the Russians would not have shown the Vostok rocket if that were still the rocket they are now using. And we do not know anything actually about later Russian rockets. As far as the bigger non-military American rockets go, the list of those we have today reads like this:

1. Titan II, an Air Force rocket that was used for the Gemini manned-spaceflight program, produces a takeoff thrust of 430,000 pounds. Even though it participated in a peaceful space project, it is mainly a military missile.

2. The Air Force's Titan IIIC rocket, on the other hand, was designed to carry things into space. The Titan III rocket has a takeoff thrust of 470,000 pounds and carries two upper stages; the second stage has a thrust of 100,000

pounds; and the final stage has a thrust of 17,000 pounds. The Titan III rocket has been used to place satellites into orbit, but it has been and will be flown mainly in the version that is called Titan IIIC. In that version the liquid-fuel Titan III is the "core rocket," and it is flanked by two solid-fuel rockets 120 inches in diameter and 75 feet long. Each of these solid-fuel units develops a thrust of 1,000,000 pounds, and when a Titan IIIC takes off, only the two solid-fuel rockets burn. The core rocket is not ignited until later, usually when the solid-fuel rockets are nearly burned out and are about to be jettisoned. Titan IIIC has placed quite a number of military communication satellites in various orbits, usually orbits quite distant from the earth.

3. The Saturn I rocket (NASA) was a liquid-fuel rocket with eight rocket engines and with a takeoff thrust of 1.3 million pounds. After ten flawless test flights it was succeeded by the Saturn IB rocket with a takeoff thrust of 1.5 million pounds. The Saturn I rocket never flew a specific mission but did carry several kinds of satellites during its test flights. The purpose of the Saturn I rocket was to develop a family of very large rockets, consisting of two different booster stages and several upper stages that could be used in a number of ways. A rocket of the Saturn type was to be flexible. It did not have two definite upper stages, but it might use two upper stages or only one, always depending on the payload. In some of the test flights one of the upper stages was even a dummy.

4. Saturn V, the largest member of the Saturn family, has a bottom stage with five rocket engines, each with as much thrust as the whole Saturn IB, or a total thrust of 7.5 million pounds. Saturn V made its first (and 100 percent successful) flight on November 9, 1967. Its first major mission was the flight to the moon at Christmas 1968 which

is known to history as Apollo 8. For that mission the S-II rocket with a thrust of an even million pounds was the second stage and a S-IVB rocket with a thrust of 200,000 pounds was the third stage.

Of course it happens quite often that a satellite weighing only 200 or 250 pounds is to be put into a fairly low orbit. Such a mission can be carried out by a smaller launch vehicle, of which NASA has two kinds.

5. The Delta rocket is a liquid-fuel rocket that began its career as a military missile named Thor. Since the Thor, with a takeoff thrust of 170,000 pounds, could carry a considerable weight, it was used for some early space missions, even (unsuccessful) attempts to shoot to the moon. The Delta rocket is a Thor designed for space missions only; it could not be used as a missile. The takeoff thrust of the Delta is the same as that of the Thor, but there is a "thrust-augmented Delta" (or "TAD") that has three solid-fuel rockets helping during the takeoff. With all three of them burning, the total takeoff thrust is 330,000 pounds.

6. The Scout rocket is the smallest of the space rockets. It also has a semi-military ancestry; its main stage is a modified form of the main stage of an early Navy Polaris missile. The Scout is a solid-fuel rocket through all its four stages; the takeoff thrust is 104,500 pounds.

While the best way of comparing various rockets is the comparison of the takeoff thrust, there is another way, too. That way is to calculate the weight of a satellite that a specific rocket could put into orbit. In order to make the calculation, one has to agree on a standard orbit. The orbit chosen is a circular orbit 100 nautical miles (115 statistic miles) above sea level. The Scout rocket could put a 300-

**69**

pound satellite into this orbit and Titan II a 7000-pound satellite. The list for the rockets mentioned looks like this:

| Rocket | Theoretical satellite weight in 115-mile orbit |
|---|---|
| Scout | 300 pounds |
| Delta | 750 ″ |
| TAD | 1,300 ″ |
| Titan II | 7,000 ″ |
| Titan IIIC | 20,000 ″ |
| Saturn I | 22,000 ″ |
| Saturn V | 240,000 ″ |

Before we conclude the discussion of the rockets, it might be useful to say something about their fuels. The fuel of the original skyrockets and of the signal rockets used during the First World War was simple old-fashioned gunpowder. The gunpowder that was used in muskets and pistols consisted of 75 percent saltpeter, 13 percent sulphur, and 12 percent pulverized charcoal. For skyrockets this mixture burned too fast and caused the rocket to explode instead of making it rise. Therefore the three ingredients were mixed in a different proportion for skyrockets, but the different version of gunpowder was called by the logical name of "rocket powder" only in military arsenals. The fireworks makers called it "lazy powder" instead, and its mixture ratio was 60 percent saltpeter, 25 percent pulverized charcoal, and 15 percent sulphur.

After the invention of smokeless powder for firearms, almost all cartridges of any size, from pocket pistols to artillery, were loaded with smokeless powder. But if somebody tried to charge a rocket with smokeless powder, all he accomplished was a fast explosion. Rockets kept relying on the old "lazy powder."

The great advance in rocket technology that began in about 1925 consisted in replacing the weak lazy powder by the much more powerful liquid fuels. Most of the early experimenters used gasoline first because it was easily available. Many rockets, among them the first large rocket, the German V-2, burned alcohol. Nowadays, the most customary liquid fuel for large rockets is high-grade kerosene. The oxidizer for all these fuels is liquid oxygen, a faintly blueish liquid that must be kept very cold if it is to stay liquid.

Some of the early experimenters were not happy about liquid oxygen. It was not the fact that it has to be kept very cold that annoyed them, because that can be done quite easily by means of insulated containers. What was annoying was that thirty years ago it was almost more difficult to buy five or ten gallons of liquid oxygen than to design and build the rocket in which the liquid oxygen was to be used. Liquid oxygen could be had in only the few cities in which a factory for air products was located, and even then one usually had to give advance notice. It is not at all surprising that experimenters carefully looked through handbooks for a substance that did not need to be kept cold to stay liquid, that contained a lot of oxygen, and that could be bought in any city. And, of course, a substance that was not expensive, or at least one that would not stay expensive.*

Unfortunately, the choice of possible substitutes for oxygen was small. There was a substance called nitrogen-tetroxide, consisting of two nitrogen and four oxygen atoms per molecule, written $N_2O_4$. Then there was nitrogenpent-oxide ($N_2O_5$), but neither substance was much used, and

* Something may be expensive because its raw materials are rare or hard to obtain. But something may be expensive because there is little demand for it and, as a result, only small amounts are produced. If the demand increases and production rises, the price will go down.

71

although they were well known as chemicals, there was little information about their behavior, especially their behavior in large quantities. Also, because they were not used much, they were not produced in quantity. Nowadays $N_2O_4$ is produced in quantity and is used in the Titan II rocket.

A substance known as hydrogen peroxide with the formula $H_2O_2$ (two hydrogen atoms and two oxygen atoms making up each molecule) looked fine on paper. It was even produced in quantity as a bleach, but what you got when you bought hydrogen peroxide in a chemical supply house was not hydrogen peroxide but a solution of hydrogen peroxide in water. The drugstore solution contained about 4 percent hydrogen peroxide; a chemical supply house might have an 8 percent solution on hand. These solutions were much too watery to be used in rocket work, and manufacturers explained that it was unwise to prepare more concentrated solutions. They had a tendency to explode, for reasons then unknown. Hydrogen peroxide seemed too dangerous to use.

It so happened that there was a scientist and inventor in Germany who insisted on getting high-strength hydrogen peroxide. He was Professor Hellmuth Walter, in Kiel, and he had obtained big contracts from the German army and navy. He forced the manufacturers to produce stronger and stronger solutions of hydrogen peroxide by promising larger and more lucrative contracts. Since the manufacturers wanted these contracts, they worked seriously on the problem of the unwanted explosions. As had been suspected by Professor Walter, the explosions were due to impurities; hydrogen peroxide of high purity did not explode, even when it was in a high-strength solution of 65 or 70 percent. In the course of the research another cause of explosions was uncovered: a high-strength solution blew up if it came into contact with copper or a copper alloy such as brass.

But the research caused by Professor Walter's offers of large contracts took place during the Second World War in Germany and did not become immediately known. Its ultimate purpose was for propulsion of submarines. Until it did become known, hydrogen peroxide had to be regarded as a dangerous substance. It is not much used even now, in spite of the fact that it is available.

For practical purposes there was only one "substitute" for liquid oxygen, namely, nitric acid. The acid has the formula $HNO_3$, which means among other things that there are 3 atoms of oxygen in every molecule. Nitric acid was produced in quantity at a low price and, though very corrosive, is quite safe once you have learned how to handle it.

In the process of trying to substitute nitric acid for oxygen in a rocket motor an interesting discovery was made. Turpentine burst into flame spontaneously when touched by nitric acid, and a liquid chemical called aniline did the same. This was not only interesting, but also useful. If one used aniline and nitric acid in a rocket, there was no need for a separate mechanism for igniting the rocket motor. This, at the very least, saved weight. The combinations of fuel and oxidizer that ignited spontaneously were called "hypergols," and the first rocket to use hypergols was the California-designed WAC-Corporal in 1947.

Chemical research on hypergols after the first flight of a WAC-Corporal rocket had two purposes. Every once in a while, a hypergolic mixture failed to ignite, so chemists began looking for a substance that was absolutely reliable as far as ignition went. They found one fairly quickly; it was "unsymmetrical dimethyl hydrazine"—trade-named "Dimazine." But the other search was not successful, namely, the attempt at finding a hypergolic combination

**73**

that would be as powerful as the simple combination of kerosene and oxygen. The known hypergols do not deliver as much thrust as the non-hypergolic combinations, and for this reason they are used in comparatively small upper-stage rockets that are carried into space by the bigger ones.

During the Second World War, chemists had succeeded in finding ways of adapting smokeless powder to rocket propulsion. The rockets in question were battlefield rockets, none of them over five feet long. Using the smokeless powder for larger missiles proved to be so difficult that it could be called impossible. Fuel chemists then had a new problem on their hands; they had to produce a fuel that was solid but not brittle (since a rocket charge with a crack in it inevitably explodes), a fuel that was powerful, that could be mixed and cured by automatic machinery, and that could be made into very large charges.

In the past, fuel chemists who made the modern types of gunpowder had been very proud of the fact that they could call their powders "smokeless." The term was not quite true; a rifle shot still produced a small cloud of smoke, but the cloud was much smaller and far less dense than the smoke cloud produced by the old-fashioned black powder. When the "smokeless" powder was adapted to aircraft and battlefield rockets, the fact that it produced little smoke was purely incidental. The smokeless powders were chosen because they were far more powerful than the old rocket powder and because the charges could be mass-produced.

The question of whether the charges for bigger missiles than battlefield rockets produced a lot of smoke or none at all was unimportant. It so happened that the new rocket fuels were quite smoky, but they grew reliable; they were powerful and they could be made very large.

In the old black rocket powder the charcoal and the

sulphur represented the fuel proper, while saltpeter, releasing oxygen when heated, represented the oxidizer. In the new rocket charges the fuel proper is synthetic rubber, while the oxidizer is a chemical that is kneaded into the rubber during manufacture. A few other substances are also added in small amounts. Some of them prevent chemical deterioration of the charge, and some increase its power. Details of the manufacture and ingredients are secrets; partly they are military secrets, partly they are manufacturers' secrets.

When the newspapers began reporting on the new rocket charges, something totally unexpected happened in the public mind. The public jumped to the conclusion that the era of liquid rocket fuels was past and that space would now be conquered by solid fuels. Rocket engineers working on new liquid-fuel engines even received letters berating them for wasting their time and the public's money.

Of course public opinion was wrong.

The eager letterwriters were wrong.

The rocket experts knew what they were doing, but they would still have liked to know just what had caused the sudden shift in attitude. I am sorry to report that no answer was found—at least, not a single answer. To some extent it may have been company-generated publicity; to some extent it may have been impressive color photographs that appeared in nationally distributed magazines. Or it may have been the word "solid" itself, sounding so solid. The largest contributing factor probably was the information that the Polaris missile that armed a fleet of new submarines was a solid-fuel rocket and that the new Minuteman missiles also were propelled by solid fuel.

The military planners had good reasons for the switchover from liquid to solid fuels, but the reason was not that solid fuel was "better." It was only better for a particular purpose. One might just as well have concluded that a tank must be "better" than a tractor.

The main reason why the military planners went in so heavily for solid fuels was that to them firing time was of the utmost importance. In case of an attack by an enemy, there was no time to pump fuel and oxidizer into the missiles. They had to be ready for the counter-strike. A solid-fuel missile is very much like a cartridge—it is ready for immediate use. In the case of missiles for the Navy there was a second reason: liquid-fuel rockets were too tall to be used on shipboard; solid-fuel missiles could be made short and squat.

If a solid-fuel rocket can be compared to a cartridge, a liquid-fuel rocket might be compared to a jet plane. It needs careful servicing and it must be fueled, which takes time. But when ready, it can be controlled very well. Once a solid-fuel rocket has been ignited, its charge will burn until it is completely consumed. A liquid-fuel rocket can be "throttled" by making the fuel pumps run more slowly. It can be shut off completely, and it can even be re-ignited; in fact, some space operations depend on temporary shutdowns followed by re-ignition.

Hence liquid-fuel rockets are still supreme when it comes to space flight. And it may be added that liquid fuels are still a little more powerful than even the most advanced solid fuels.

Liquid fuels are much cheaper. Pound for pound, solid fuels cost about ten times as much as liquid fuels. Unfortunately, the rocket for liquid fuels is more expensive than the rocket for solid fuels.

It is interesting to compare the two types of rockets on the basis of cost. For every thousand dollars of the price of a rocket, only $13 goes for fuel in a liquid-fuel rocket, but $155 goes for fuel in a solid-fuel rocket. The following breakdown shows what costs how much:

| LIQUID-FUEL ROCKET | | SOLID FUEL ROCKET | |
|---|---|---|---|
| | per $1000 of total cost | | |
| Rocket engine, | | Casing | 214 |
| pumps, etc. | 795 | Nozzle | 100 |
| Tanks | 76 | Structure | 531 |
| Structure | 116 | Fuel | 155 |
| Fuel | 13 | | $1000 |
| | $1000 | | |

And how much does a rocket shot cost?

There is no answer to that question, because it varies almost from shot to shot. But two figures can be given. When the American Telegraph & Telephone Company asked the government to put its Telstar satellite into orbit, the government charged the company two million dollars. The rocket used was a Thor with upper stages. And when the West German government wanted to put a heavy satellite into orbit, which would have required an Atlas rocket to lift it, the Air Force asked for five million dollars.

The Germans did not buy the rocket, but the Air Force offer provides an idea about the cost.

# CHAPTER VI

# The First Years of the New Moons

IT would be a pleasure if one could say in retrospect that the United States pioneered the space age. Unfortunately, it wasn't so at all. There was no official encouragement, and if it had not been for a number of individuals, most of them engineers or scientists of one kind or another, the United States would have been totally unprepared when the time came to carry out long-established ideas.

In part this was the fault of one man, Dr. Vannevar Bush, who had done a great deal of work for the government during the Second World War. As late as 1953 he told a Congressional committee that he wished that people would stop talking about rockets with a ballistic range of 3000 miles. He declared that such rockets were about twenty years in the future, if they were in the future at all. The Congressmen naturally believed Dr. Bush who, to them, was the "voice of science." But only two years later rumors began to circulate that the Russians were testing rockets with a range of 900 miles (these were the Pobyeda rockets), and a year later the rumors said that the range of

Russian missiles had been increased to 1500 miles. We now know that the reports were correct, if incomplete, but at the time the Administration tried to brush them aside as "unfounded."

While the government of the United States retreated into secrecy, scientific organizations in all countries were busy making plans for a big scientific event. It was called the International Geophysical Year, which was to run from July 1, 1957, to the end of 1958. The IGY, as it was called for short, was a follow-up of a similar international scientific collaboration that had taken place twenty-five years earlier. That earlier effort had been called the Antarctic Year—also South Polar Year—and had been devoted to the exploration of Antarctica and the waters around it. The IGY was to explore the whole earth, the oceans, and the atmosphere.

At about that time the American Rocket Society sent a memorandum to the National Academy of Science, pointing out that the exploration of the upper atmosphere should include the exploration of nearby space, hence the planning for the IGY should contain plans for an artificial satellite. Some of the members of the Academy had had thoughts along similar lines, and in July 1955 President Eisenhower announced that the United States would put an artificial satellite into orbit during the IGY. The name of the project was Project Vanguard, and it was managed by the Navy. The Russians kept quiet at the moment. But by Christmas 1955 they said that they had satellite plans, too.

In the course of the year 1956 the Vanguard rocket was built in three different places. Its first stage was a liquid-fuel rocket burning alcohol with liquid oxygen, based on the Viking rocket the Navy had built and tested during the years from 1949 to 1955. Of the twelve Viking rockets one had been a weird failure (the rocket tore itself loose during a static test), and three had been partial failures, but the others had been successful. It must be mentioned that there were two versions of the Viking rocket; the first seven were quite tall and slender, and only three of them performed well. The rockets numbered VIII through XII were less tall and had a larger diameter, and all of them performed well, with the exception of number VIII, which is the one that took off when it was not supposed to do so. There were two more Viking rockets of the second type, but they were not used in the Viking program. They were the first two shots in the Vanguard program, fired for testing instrumentation both in the rocket and on the ground.

The Viking rockets had been built by the Martin Company in Baltimore, and the same company built the first stage of the Vanguard. The second stage was also a liquid-fuel rocket, burning Dimazine with nitric acid; it was built in California by Aerojet, Inc. The third stage was a solid-fuel rocket built by Hercules Powder Co. on the East Coast. The third stage was to carry the artificial satellite, and the whole rocket would stand about 70 feet tall when assembled.

This had the perfectly logical result that the Army and the Air Force were thinking about artificial satellites, too. But Eisenhower's Secretary of Defense, Charles Wilson, a glib and brusque millionaire,* told both the Army and the Air Force that he would not permit them to shoot satellites into space. He said that the United States had a satellite program, namely, Project Vanguard, and that they were not to compete with it. Then he did his best to starve the Navy's Project Vanguard for funds.

Because of his official position, Charles Wilson could

* A science advisor said that he had never met a man as uninformed as Wilson and had also never met a man so determined to stay that way.

keep the Army and the Air Force from shooting satellites; he could not keep them from thinking about satellites. The Air Force quietly prepared to use its new and not quite finished Thor rockets for shooting to the moon—as soon as the Thor was ready and Wilson was out of the way. The Army built upper stages for its Redstone rocket and called it Jupiter C, pretending that it was only to be used for testing components for the Jupiter missile then under development. On September 20, 1956, "Missile 27," one of the Jupiter C rockets, made a record shot over a distance of 3100 miles. Its top stage had no ignition, as per order. If it had been ignited, it would have become the first artificial satellite.

On October 4, 1957, the Russians sent Sputnik I into orbit.

On October 23, 1957, the first Vanguard rocket made a successful flight; unfortunately, only its booster stage actually was a rocket, the two upper stages carried by the booster being dummies; the upper stages were not yet ready for flight testing.

On November 3, 1957, the Russians put Sputnik II into orbit.

By that time the "resignation" of Charles Wilson had been announced, and Neil McElroy had been appointed as his successor. Now one could *work!*

But accidents will happen.

The first complete Vanguard rocket lost thrust immediately after takeoff on December 6, 1957, fell over, burst open, and burned on the pad.

On January 31, 1958, a Jupiter C (Army) rocket put the first American satellite, Explorer I, into orbit around the earth.

On March 17, 1958, a naval Vanguard rocket put a tiny "test satellite" into orbit; it became satellite Vanguard I.

**81**

On March 26, 1958, the Army followed suit with Explorer III; the second Explorer had failed to reach orbit because the upper stages had fired in the wrong direction.

On May 15, 1958, the Russians countered with Sputnik III, which made the American satellites look ridiculous, because it weighed 2925 pounds. The Vanguard test satellite weighted 3¼ pounds and the Explorer satellites about 31 pounds apiece, and that weight included the weight of the casing of the top stage.

Explorer IV followed on July 26, 1958.

On December 18, 1958, the United States orbited its first "big one," a whole Atlas missile (the Air Force secret rocket) without the two booster engines, weighing 8750 pounds. This was Project Score, a surprise to friend and foe alike. Even the firing crew (with very few exceptions) had not known that this Atlas rocket was fired for orbit. One tracker, watching a computer device called the Impact Predicter, concluded that his instrument had to be out of order because it told him that there would be no impact.

It was the last satellite shot during the IGY, though Score was no part of the IGY. One has to keep in mind that the IGY ended on the last day of 1958 and that was the reason for some new organizational measures, specifically for the founding of NASA, the National Aeronautics and Space Administration.

Originally the American satellites, that is to say Project Vanguard, were meant to be in the framework of the IGY and therefore in the domain of the National Academy of Science. The responsibility for the actual shooting had been given to the Navy; the Army and its Jupiter C had been called in as an emergency because the Vanguard Program was so slow in taking shape. After Explorer IV had been orbited, the Vanguard Program still had five shots to go. It was very likely that it would run into the year 1959;

actually, the second Vanguard satellite was orbited on February 17, 1959, after the IGY was over.

Meanwhile, the Air Force had succeeded in having both the Thor and the Atlas missiles in working order, and the Army was eager to try its Juno, which was the new Jupiter missile with extra upper stages. The President faced the choice of letting the Army and the Air Force compete with each other in satellite shooting while the Navy Vanguard program was still running, or else putting somebody in charge of space shots.

The thought that there should be a government agency for space research was fairly unanimous. But what kind of an agency should it be? It could be another armed service, called, say, U.S. Space Force. Or else it could be a civilian agency like the Atomic Energy Commission. President Eisenhower decided in favor of a civilian agency, but he did not, as most observers expected, create a new agency; he ordered an old one reorganized. Since the days of the First World War there had been a scientific agency called N.A.C.A., or National Advisory Committee on Aeronautics. N.A.C.A. had investigated problems of flight and had published its findings so that airplane builders and airplane pilots could take advantage of the results of N.A.C.A.'s work. Of course, by 1958 there were not many uninvestigated problems in the field of aviation left.

Therefore the new agency, slated to begin its existence and its work on October 1, 1958, was to work in the field of space research *and* to take care of remaining aeronautical problems. Hence it was called NASA, for National Aeronautics and Space Administration. NASA was not only to cover two fields (later on, underwater research was added); it also was to do the research *and* the development, something to which some old-line employees of N.A.C.A. objected.

**83**

However, the organization of such a large agency takes time, and NASA did not take over what was already planned by the services. The Navy still finished up Project Vanguard, while the Air Force had a whole satellite program mapped out. In the case of the Air Force, there were other reasons, too. At one point the Secretary of Defense had ordered that the Air Force was to be in charge of all long-range missiles—everything that could shoot at targets more than 200 miles distant. It would have served no purpose to rescind this order, but it was amended to refer only to missiles that were launched from a base on land. Shipborne missiles were a separate story. So the Air Force had to stay in charge of long-range missiles, since NASA was a civilian agency that had nothing to do with weapons development. And since satellites for military purposes were a distinct possibility, the Air Force could also shoot military satellites. It should be mentioned that the Air Force had also hoped to be in charge of manned space flight, but that was assigned to NASA.

While NASA mainly concentrated on its own organization and on Project Mercury, the first manned-spaceflight program, the other satellite programs kept going. The Vanguard Program reached its end with the orbiting of the 50-pound Vanguard III on September 18, 1959. The Explorer satellites of the Army had been taken over by NASA. But on February 28, 1959, the Air Force had launched Discoverer I, to be followed by Discoverer II on April 13, 1959, presumably using Thor rockets. They were the first satellites to be put into polar orbits, and they had to be fired from an Air Force base on the West Coast.

The reason was that even the most careful planning cannot overcome geographical facts if the latter happen to be in the way. When NASA was organized, there were three rocket proving grounds * in the United States. There was the White Sands Proving Ground in New Mexico, where almost all the V-2s and most of the Navy Viking rockets had been fired, but which, being inland, was not suitable for satellite shots. There was Vandenberg Air Force Base in California for Air Force missiles, and there was the Atlantic Missile Range based at Cape Canaveral in Florida, also an Air Force installation. All the American satellites up to Discoverer I had been orbited from there.

The scheme to be followed was: The White Sands Proving Ground would be used for tactical Army missiles, both for development and for troop training for such missiles with ranges of less than 150 miles. Vandenberg Air Force Base was for Air Force missiles and for training. Everything experimental with a long range, whether Air Force or NASA, would go to the Range; since the Discoverer satellites were certainly experimental, they should have been fired from that range, but it was at that point that the geographical hitch showed up. There was no problem in firing Explorer satellites into an orbit with an inclination of about 30 degrees; the booster stage of the rocket would fall into the Atlantic Ocean.

For putting a satellite into a polar orbit, with an inclination of 90 degrees or close to it, it did not matter in theory whether one fired northward or southward; in either case, an orbit going over both poles would be the result. In practice, however, a polar orbit shot fired northward from the Cape would deposit the booster stage of the rocket near the shore of Georgia, and one could not promise that it would be on the seaward side of the shore. Firing south-

* Not counting two Navy installations, Inyokern and Point Mugu, both in California; but these were for smaller military rockets.

ward from the Cape carried the danger that the booster stage might fall on Cuba.

Fired from the West Coast, a northward shot also would make the booster stage fall on land, but a southward shot was safe. Due south of the Vandenberg firing site, there is nothing but water until Antarctica is reached.

The first Discoverer of the Air Force tumbled in orbit and stayed in orbit for only five days; it simply was not a success. One special feature of the Discoverer Program was that the satellites were to eject capsules after a number of orbits. These capsules were to re-enter the atmosphere and release a parachute so that they could be recovered. The Air Force had modified a number of aircraft for this recovery. They had two long booms extending from an airplane, with a rope stretched between the tips of the booms. If everything went well, the rope would catch the shrouds of the parachute of the de-orbited capsule. The second Discoverer did eject its capsule, but something went wrong with the timing devices. The capsule was to be ejected over Hawaii, but it actually was ejected over Spitsbergen, the largest of a group of islands to the north of Scandinavia. It was never found.

There was much to be learned before the maneuver succeeded, and a series of failures had to be accepted. Discoverers III and IV failed to attain orbit. Discoverers V and VI did go into orbit, numero V on August 13, 1959, and numero VI six days later, on August 19. Both dutifully ejected their capsules, but in both cases the transmitters in the capsules failed to work, and with silent transmitters in the capsules it would have been just a case of very good luck if one of the recovery aircraft had sighted a capsule. Discoverers IX and X did not reach orbit; Discoverers VII, VIII, and XI did, but recovery of the capsule was not accomplished. Discoverer XII failed to reach orbit. Discoverer XIII took off smoothly on August 10, 1960, and it was the capsule of this thirteenth Discoverer which was the first to be recovered. It was fished from the ocean about 25 hours after takeoff.

Discoverer XIV went into orbit on August 18, 1960, and on the following day the Air Force could announce that it had succeeded in catching the capsule in mid-air. The crew of the recovery airplane even succeeded in taking pictures of the re-entry. Discoverer XV was sent into orbit on September 13, 1960. It ejected its capsule in the right place and at the right time the next day; the recovery planes saw it float down to the ocean, but it sank before the airplanes could reach it. But the next Discoverer, XVII, on November 12, 1960, yielded the second mid-air catch on November 14.

Discoverer XIX did not carry a capsule. It was orbited as a test for the Midas missile-detection system; it served as the target for the new detection system and then was left to "decay" naturally, which it did about a month later. (See table in the Appendix.) Discoverer XX misbehaved, and broke into four pieces. The next one, Discoverer XXI, again carried no capsule; its purpose was to test whether the rocket engine could be re-started in space. When Discoverer XXIII did what it did, the ground crews and trackers had to realize that a problem that has been solved does not necessarily stay solved: it ejected its capsule in the wrong direction!

There followed four successful recoveries.

The capsule of numero XXV was recovered from the ocean after it had completed 33 orbits around the earth. Numero XXVI produced the fourth mid-air catch after 32 orbits, numero XXIX was recovered from the ocean after 33 orbits, and numero XXX resulted in the fifth mid-air catch on September 15, 1961, after 33 orbits. Two more capsules were recovered from later flights, both from the ocean and both after 17 orbits in space, those of Discoverer XXXII and Discoverer XXXV.

Discoverer XXXVI, orbited on December 12, 1961, did something new: it carried what is called a piggyback payload. That payload was a small satellite named Oscar, specifically designed for amateur radio operators to test their equipment. The capsule of numero XXXVI was recovered on December 16; Oscar was left in orbit. It re-entered on January 31, 1962. The Discoverer satellite proper, minus the capsule and minus Oscar, lasted a few weeks longer in space; it re-entered on March 8, 1962.

In December 1961 it had been announced that Discoverer XXXVI would be the last of the series. But a few more were to come. Numero XXXVII failed to reach orbit; numero XXXVIII did, but the Air Force did not announce the orbit, only that it had re-entered on March 21, 1962. And then, on July 28, 1962, there was one more shot that was not called a Discoverer but went into an orbit greatly resembling the orbits of earlier Discoverer shots.

Then the program was really over.

What had the Russians been doing in the meantime?

They had their Sputnik program, which, though it had been first, was somewhat slow in getting underway. The first Sputnik had been spherical, with a weight of 183.6 pounds. The second had been conical, with an overall weight of 1120 pounds. It consisted of two parts, firmly attached to each other. One of these parts was an instrumented sphere, a duplicate of the first Sputnik; the second held a live dog named Laika ("barker") with instruments attached to its body. These instruments measured heart beat, rate of breathing, and blood pressure. After one hundred hours in orbit when the batteries in the satellite began to run down—batteries accounted for much of the weight of the satellite—the dog was painlessly put to death, and both Russian and American scientists waited for the orbit to decay. The natural decay of an orbit was the only way of estimating the density of the upper layers of the atmosphere. Sputnik II lasted much longer in orbit than Sputnik I. The first Sputnik had been orbited on the 4th of October, 1957, and had re-entered on January 4, 1958. The second Sputnik, orbited on November 3, 1957, did not re-enter until April 14, 1958. This was because of its greater mass; obviously a heavier body is less handicapped by faint air resistance than a lighter body.*

Sputnik III, the heavyweight, followed on May 15, 1958. It carried scientific instruments and batteries only, and its main purpose was to measure radiation in space between the perigee (135 miles) and the apogee (1167 miles). It was the only Russian satellite for the whole year of 1958, and Russian scientists wrote voluminously on the results obtained.

It may be useful to say at this point that the Russians do publish the results of their work in space, though they are often slow about it. But they publish only information about the satellites, their instrumentation, and the facts discovered by these instruments. They never say a word about the rockets that put the satellites into orbit, presumably because these are the same rockets that are also their missiles and therefore under military secrecy.

Sputnik IV was orbited on May 15, 1960; there had been no Soviet orbital shots in all of 1959.

* During the preliminary discussions of the Vanguard Program it had been intended to test this directly. Along with the spherical Vanguard satellite, weighing 21½ pounds, a spherical balloon of the same diameter but with a weight of only three ounces was to be orbited. Their orbits would decay at different rates. It was an interesting plan, but for reasons not known to me it was not carried out.

Sputnik IV was another heavyweight, falling short of an even 10,000 pounds by only about 12 pounds. Western trackers were surprised to find that some time later Sputnik IV was in another orbit. Then it broke up into what looked like one large piece and at least eight smaller, but still large, pieces. The Russians did not give out too much information, but what they did say and an analysis of the satellite's behavior made it clear where the Russian space program was going.

Sputnik IV had been a prototype of a space cabin; that is, a spacecraft that would ultimately carry people. The space cabin, of course, had retro rockets for slowing down in orbit and for re-entering the atmosphere. But the retro rockets had pointed in the wrong direction when they were ignited, so the craft had been accelerated and the orbit became larger, raising the apogee from 222 to 412 miles. Just why it then broke apart never became clear and seems to be unclear even to the Russians themselves. But the fact that it was a space cabin made the Russian program clear. Numero I had been simply a test; numero II had tested a living organism that is high in the evolutionary scale. The test proved that a dog could survive, and where a dog can survive a man can, too. Numero III had checked on radiation in space, which was then thought to be a major hazard; after numero III had shown that it was not, the Russians could go ahead with the design of a manned ship. That this first prototype had a few weaknesses was not in the program, but that is how one learns to design something better.

If this reasoning was correct, Sputnik V would be another prototype for a manned ship. It was.

Sputnik V was orbited on August 19, 1960, and assumed a circular orbit not quite 200 miles above sea level. The retro rockets were fired the next day; the craft was slowed

90

down, re-entered, and landed on Russian territory. After it had landed, the Russians jubilantly told the world that there had been two dogs aboard which showed no ill effects after their voyage. Also aboard had been smaller laboratory animals and a few bottles of microscopic life forms, both animal and vegetable.

If all this was leading up to manned space flight—something hardly anybody doubted any more after Sputnik V— one could expect Sputnik VI to be a repeat. It was a repeat, but also a setback. The satellite, again carrying two dogs and many small life forms, slowed down in orbit with retro rockets as planned, but it burned up on re-entry.

Another repeat could be expected.

But Sputnik VII was not a repeat of Sputnik VI. It went into orbit on February 4, 1961, and then did absolutely nothing; at least, that is how it looked to the Western Hemisphere. We can be quite sure now that our impression that something had malfunctioned was correct, because on February 12, 1961, Sputnik VIII went into orbit and fired a space probe. Sputnik VIII was the "back-up" for Sputnik VII the Russians had held in reserve. The satellite re-entered on February 25, 1961 (one day before the re-entry of the useless Sputnik VII) while the space probe was on its way to Venus. Either its instruments or its transmitters failed to work; the probe is now in orbit around the sun. Its perihelion is 66.7 million miles from the sun, its aphelion 94.6 million miles from the sun, or outside the earth's orbit by about 100,000 miles, and its orbital period is an even 300 days.

This was the first use of what came to be called the "parking orbit"—an orbit around the earth for a carrier spacecraft which then, at the right moment, launches a space probe to the moon or to another planet. The Russians have a special fondness for parking orbits; they use them virtually every time they want to send a space probe away from earth. We have used parking orbits, too, though not as often.

Since numeros VII and VIII had served a different purpose than advancing the date of the first manned flight, everybody wondered what the ninth Sputnik would do. Would it be a continuation of the original program, or would it again serve a different purpose? When it took off on March 9, 1961, the Russians themselves removed all speculation by calling it *korabl-sputnik; korabl* is the Russian form of "caravel," a sailing vessel. It was to be a spaceship. Again there was a dog with smaller life forms aboard. It was de-orbited and brought to a safe landing after a few orbits. The problem no longer was to see whether a dog could live in orbit—it was how to bring it back safely.

Sputnik X also was called *korabl-sputnik* and was launched on March 25, 1961. It was a precise repeat of numero IX and marked the end of the series of satellites called Sputnik. Since the Russians had obviously mastered their technique of de-orbiting and safe landing after re-entry, a manned flight would be next. The only question left in the minds of Western observers was: How soon?

It was very soon. On April 12, only eighteen days after Sputnik X, Yuri Alekseyevitch Gagarin took off in Vostok I and flew one orbit around the earth. Since he landed about 200 miles to the west of his takeoff site, it was not quite a full orbit, but to the Russians this did not matter. Their Sputnik Program had done what it was supposed to do: lead to manned space flight.

# CHAPTER VII

# Discoveries of the Satellites

THE two satellites of 1957, the six of 1958, and the ten of 1959 had one thing in common, even though they seemed to be quite different. They were of greatly different weights, and they traveled in widely different orbits (one Russian satellite in 1959 even made one loop around the moon), but they all were research satellites.

The purpose of a research satellite is to learn something that cannot be learned in any other way. This was remarkably demonstrated by the very first American satellite, which made an entirely unexpected discovery. Satellite Explorer I orbited with its perigee at 224 miles and its apogee at 1573 miles. Among the instruments aboard was one that measured natural radiation in space. It soon turned out that this instrument fell silent at regular intervals. When the satellite was near its perigee, the instrument worked fine, and as the satellite receded from the earth the radiation count gradually went up. It reached a fairly high level—and then it fell silent. An hour or so later it came to life again.

The behavior was checked carefully by Dr. James A. Van Allen of Iowa State University. He had experience with rays in space; in fact, he had made a very useful invention for their investigation. He had thought of rockets for carrying the instruments to a high altitude, but the only available rocket at the time, one that could be carried along on shipboard, was a solid-fuel rocket that could reach only an altitude of 60,000 feet. Van Allen conceived the idea of having the rocket carried to an altitude of about 60,000 feet by a light and inexpensive plastic balloon. When the balloon had reached its ceiling, which was somewhere between 50,000 and 60,000 feet, the rocket was fired by radio command. At that altitude most of the earth's atmosphere was below the rocket, so it could move unhampered by air resistance and carry the instruments to altitudes of around 60 miles.

The research was concerned with cosmic rays, the subatomic particles (mostly protons, the nuclei of hydrogen atoms) which had been observed more frequently in high latitudes. The theory was that the earth's magnetic field deflected these protons, except at the North and South Poles. The so-called "lines" of the field are not straight; they curve in toward the magnetic poles. Popular writers, hearing about these ideas at the time, jumped to the conclusion that the earth's magnetic poles "attracted" the protons. This was nonsense. The magnetic lines, curving in toward the magnetic poles, produced a kind of funnel where the protons could come in. Van Allen's experiments with his "rockoons," as he called the combination of balloon and rocket, were undertaken to see whether this theory was correct. It was.

Now the same young physicist was confronted with the inexplicable behavior of the instrument aboard Explorer I. While Explorer I had given the first indications, the evidence was made definite by Explorer III, which recorded the radiation intensity on tapes which were then duplicated on the ground. Examining literally miles of tapes, he noticed that the satellite had been about 600 miles from the ground when the instrument stopped. It was at about the same altitude when the instrument started reporting again. Then he had the idea that was to solve the problem: Could it be that the instrument stopped reporting because it was overloaded at those distances? He took another instrument of the same type and "overloaded" it in the laboratory by throwing X-rays at it. At a certain load the instrument stopped reporting.

Van Allen realized immediately that the earth's magnetic field did more than provide proton funnels over the magnetic poles. Apparently it trapped sub-atomic particles and held them in a wide belt over the equator. If that was correct, the center line of the belt would be the magnetic equator, which is not quite in the same position as the geographical equator. The width of the belt was found to be from 40 degrees latitude north to 40 degrees latitude south. Its thickness was still unknown.

Other physicists began calling it the Van Allen Belt almost immediately. It is still known by that name, except that we now speak about the Inner Van Allen Belt, because one of the Air Force attempts to shoot to the moon resulted in the discovery of an Outer Van Allen belt about 12,000 miles from the earth.*

The next problem for Van Allen was just what kind of radiation in his belt overloaded the instrument. Theoretically, both electrons and protons could form the belt. The

* The lunar probe was called Pioneer III, launched on December 6, 1958. It did not reach the moon because it was not quite fast enough. Its maximum altitude was 66,654 miles; it re-entered over equatorial Africa and burned up 38 hours and 6 minutes after take-off.

result would be the same, but electrons and protons would act differently on the instrument. Protons would overload it directly. Electrons would do it by producing X-rays.

To understand the mechanism we have to look at an X-ray tube. The glass tube itself has only the purpose of maintaining the vacuum inside the tube, to keep the air out. Then there is a stream of free electrons which strikes the metal "target" at the other end of the tube. The impact of the electrons causes the target to emit X-rays. Since this was first observed by a German, Professor Konrad Röntgen, the phenomenon received a German name: *Bremsstrahlung,* which means the radiation (that is the X-rays) caused by the target's "braking" the motion of the electrons. Van Allen pointed out that at an altitude of 600 miles you had the conditions inside an X-ray tube: you had a vacuum, you had a stream of freely moving electrons and, if you orbited a satellite at that altitude, you added the "target." Van Allen said that it was probably mainly *Bremsstrahlung.* He used the German term—its English equivalent is "impact radiation." Later on, however, he decided that it was mostly protons that constituted his belt.

Not every one of the early satellites produced such a startling discovery, but the story of Explorer I shows what a research satellite can do. Of course, a discovery can be negative. One of our probes sent to the planet Venus discovered, for example, that the chance of being struck by a grain-sized meteorite in interplanetary space is very, very slight. Nobody had known before whether the chance of being struck would be small or fairly large; Venus probe Mariner II settled the point.

Another discovery of the early space age was furnished by Russia's Cosmic Rocket II, which was the first man-made object to strike the moon, on September 14, 1959.

It reported, before it was smashed into very small pieces by the impact, that our moon does not have a magnetic field.

Since the purpose of satellites was to learn about space, most of the satellites orbited during the first six years of the space age were research satellites. Even now, many research satellites are sent into space. There is always something new to look for, or earlier findings to be verified. Sometimes earlier findings have to be discounted, as for example the earlier statistics about meteoritic dust in the vicinity of the earth.

That tiny meteorites, the size of a grain of sand or smaller, orbited the sun was a known astronomical fact. It was known that there are "swarms" of them, the leftovers of former small comets that had been slowly torn apart by the gravitational fields of other and larger bodies in space, mainly the sun. But how many dust particles were there outside these "swarms"? A meteorite detector was designed; it would report impacts of such tiny meteorites. The picture that gradually emerged was that cosmic dust seemed to be concentrated around the earth and that there was much less of it a long distance from the earth. Our planet seemed to be surrounded by a thin ring of cosmic dust. Astronomers who were well acquainted with the history of their own science recalled that the German astronomer Wilhelm Klinkerfues, during the latter part of the nineteenth century, had predicted that such a dust ring would be found. Klinkerfues even thought that it might be visible if one could look at the earth from a long distance, say from the moon.

But then it was found during tests in the laboratory that the meteorite detector sent out its bright electronic *ping* not only when struck, but also when it was subjected to a sudden change in temperature. When the satellite entered the shadow of the earth, and when it came out of the shadow again and was exposed to sunlight, the instrument often recorded this fact as if it were a meteorite impact. Of course, some of the pings *were* impacts, but we cannot tell how many pings were wrong reports, so they must all be distrusted.

By 1960 satellites were sent into orbits that were not research satellites but belonged to another family. It did not have a general name, at first, but this other family of satellites is now known collectively as "applications satellites." They don't detect something new; they do a job, like transmitting messages.

There are four basic types of such applications satellites, and the United States pioneered in all of them. In fact, they all made their first appearance during the year 1960, which indicates that there must have been a great deal of private scientific speculation about useful satellites at a time when many doubted that artificial satellites could be realized at all.

The four basic types are:

*Weather Satellites.* First to be orbited was Tiros I on April 1, 1960;

*Navigational Satellites.* First to be orbited was Transit IB on April 13, 1960;

*Surveillance Satellites.* Mostly, but not exclusively, military in nature; first to be orbited was Midas II on May 24, 1960;

*Communications Satellites.* Some of them military; first to be orbited was Echo I on August 12, 1960.

Let us take them in the order in which the first prototypes were put into space.

The Weather Satellites really began with complaints

about weather forecasts that turned out to be wrong. When confronted with such complaints, meteorologists did not have a simple answer. Before they could say what had gone wrong, they had to explain the fundamentals of their science.

Partly because of the rotation of the earth, and partly because there is sunlight over half of the earth and night over the other half, weather is steadily on the move. It moves in the shape of large quantities of air, called air masses. For example, an air mass from Canada may move southward across the Great Lakes into the Middle West; it is likely to be colder than the air it encounters and is also likely to be less moist. The fundamental fact to remember whenever weather is under discussion is that warm air can hold more moisture than cold air. So if, during the summer, a colder air mass collides with a warmer and wetter air mass, the warmer air will be cooled off. Since it cannot hold as much moisture after being cooled as it could while warm, rain is the obvious result. Everybody knows that a heat wave usually "breaks" with the sound of heavy rains.

What the weather forecaster has to know are the characteristics (warm or cold, wet or dry) of the air masses, their direction of motion, and their rate of motion. Weather forecasts that were theoretically correct have gone wrong in reality because a moving air mass suddenly moved much more slowly than expected. All of which means that the forecaster, in order to make a forecast, has to know precisely what the situation is at that moment. But very often the meteorologist needs to know the weather situation in an area of the earth where there is nobody to tell him what the weather is like.

Just about three quarters of the earth's surface is ocean, and the weather over the ocean areas was, as a rule, unknown to the meteorologist. Both transport airliners and ocean liners travel specific routes, so only very narrow strips of the oceans were covered. And even the land was largely not covered by weather reporting stations. You had a good network of weather stations over the United States, eastern Canada, the coastline of western Canada, the coastlines along South America, all of Europe and European Russia, the north coast and the southern tip of Africa, some of southern Asia, and western Australia. All of it added up, at most, to five percent of the earth's surface. But to obtain just all the weather reports from the United States and Canada took all the time the forecaster had, and sometimes it took more.

If we could see the movement of air masses from space, a meteorologist could get a general picture at a glance, and then he could check with the ground stations along the path of the air masses that especially interest him and are important to the forecast. This is how the idea of the weather satellites was born.

The Tiros satellites did what was expected of them. They supplied ground stations with pictures of the cloud cover of the earth and successive pictures of the same area, taken about 1½ hours apart, furnishing clues as to the movement of the air masses. Such series of pictures would give both the direction and the speed of the air masses. Some meteorologists said that the Tiros satellites overdid it; they furnished so many pictures that time was lost in finding the important ones among the multitudes of pictures that gushed down from space. In 78 days Tiros I sent 22,952 cloud mass photographs!

Later Tiros and ESSA satellites were just as fruitful, but the weather still managed to spring some surprises on forecasters. The shortcoming was that the satellites could not tell what the air masses did over the dark half of the earth. But there is a way out: photography by infrared light, or by heat rays, if you prefer. All the weather satellites after ESSA IX will report on the dark half of the earth, as well as on the illuminated hemisphere.

The idea of the Navigational Satellite, as we have seen, was conceived a hundred years ago by the Reverend Hale (see page 4). Of course, he only wrote a story, and it could not have been done in his day, but if it could have been done, it would have been useless. The enemy of the navigator at sea is local bad weather. A cover of very low clouds may extend for just 100 square miles, but the navigator of a ship below that cloud cover is helpless. In order to find his position he has to be able to see the stars, or at least the sun, in daytime. And under such a cloud cover an orbiting "brick moon" would be as useless as the real moon.

The advantage of a modern artificial satellite is that you don't have to see it to know where it is. The satellite tells its position by radio waves, and radio waves have no trouble penetrating clouds or fog. The principle is quite simple. The navigational satellite (NavSat to the Navy) is in a well-known orbit, and the navigator on shipboard knows (from tables) where it should be in the sky beyond the clouds at a given moment. He knows where it should be, that is, if he has guessed correctly his own position on the seas. Then he sends out an "interrogatory signal" to which the satellite responds. Now the navigator knows the actual direction to the satellite from the reply he has received. The reply, let us say, comes from three degrees farther south than the navigator had expected. This means that the ship's position is three degrees farther north than the navigator had thought.

The system of navigating with the aid of an artificial satellite is now in use. It is, as the Navy says, "operational."

Once the idea had been conceived that one could watch cloud cover from space, it was evident that one could also watch areas of the ground that did not have a cloud cover. One could see what a potential enemy might be doing, unless he did it under cloud cover or in the darkness of night. Even then, the takeoff of a large missile would be visible. Or if not visible, it would give itself away because of the heat generated. The Surveillance Satellites are based on this principle. Since they are military satellites, no detail about them has been made public, except that they are there and that they have detected and reported takeoffs of our own big rockets.

But not all surveillance is military in nature.

The "earth resources" satellites (still in the future at the moment of writing) will be both peaceful and useful.

To a man walking on the ground, grass is green and leaves are green. Of course, the green of fresh grass is somewhat different from the green of old grass, and the leaves of different trees also have different degrees of greenness. But from high-flying airplanes one could see that the green of one area was not quite the same green as the green of another area. Sometimes the difference was just caused by more or less moisture in the ground. But such a difference could also mean the presence of certain minerals, and these minerals could be important. Because minerals give themselves away, it is possible to search for them from the air, or by satellite.

The search will begin by the taking of pictures with several cameras at the same time, each one loaded with a film that is especially sensitive to certain colors. That does not mean that the film, or the negatives, will be color pictures;

in fact, they may look especially drab. But what shows on those pictures is the result of that particular color having been present. Of course, a ground party will then have to complete the job, but the pictures will prevent ground parties from wasting their time in areas where there is nothing to be found.

Such pictures may also have agricultural value. They may point out that fields that are traditionally planted with corn could produce a much more valuable crop.

Finally, such an earth resources satellite, equipped with instruments for the detection of heat, however faint, may be used for the mapping of volcanic areas. It may reveal that in a certain place there is hot lava not too far underground, even though at the surface there is no indication of such hidden volcanism. Such a map of the earth could be valuable for two reasons. One is a warning of possible danger. On the other hand, subterranean hot magma can be valuable. In Italy, Iceland, and New Zealand volcanic heat is utilized to produce electric power. It is quite possible that an area that needs electric power but has no large rivers that can be dammed up for power production has a supply of subterranean heat available of which nothing is known at the surface.

And now we come to the story of the Communications Satellites, or "comsats." Long-range communication is a comparatively recent invention—about a century old by now. The people of a century ago could see the need for such communications—especially in the case of Europe and the United States—but it was both difficult and expensive. Cables had to be laid on the bottom of the ocean, or else telegraph wires had to be strung across the continent. And cables and wires were not only expensive, but also vulnerable. If there was a break in a cable anywhere, everything and everybody had to wait until it was found and repaired.

Around the turn of the century, radio was invented and became a means of communications during, and partly because of, the First World War. But it was longwave radio, now in use only for entertainment broadcasting where long range is not needed. Long-range longwave radio was cumbersome and not always reliable. The introduction of shortwave radio for communications was a step forward, but it trailed a few new problems in its wake. The shortwave radio beam could not follow the earth's curvature, so radio engineers had to make use of another natural phenomenon to reach points beyond the horizon. Near the top of our atmosphere there are several layers that are ionized, meaning that the gas molecules of the atmosphere, or at least a fair percentage of them, carry an electric charge. Such ionized gas will reflect radio waves of certain wavelengths, opening the possibility of an "ionosphere bounce." The radio beam was aimed upward at a slant so that it would be reflected by these layers in the upper atmosphere. It was the reflected beam that reached distant points.

The problem was that this looked better on paper than in reality. The reflecting layers changed their altitude with the time of day, requiring constant adjustments of the beaming angle. To make it worse, some of them occasionally "disappeared." They did not actually disappear, but lost their ability to reflect a radio beam.

If one wanted truly reliable communications by means of shortwave radio, communications independent of the time of day and the weather, one had to build relay towers on the ground so that the beam was passed on from one relay tower to the next one. Such a system would be reliable. It would also be expensive. Thinking about the expense prompted Arthur C. Clarke, then chairman of the British Interplanetary Society and not yet the world-famous

**104**

science fiction writer he was to become, to think of relays in orbit. He first expressed his thought in a published letter to a British radio magazine and then expanded it into an article that was published in 1945 in the British magazine *Wireless World*.

Clarke proposed three radio relay satellites in the synchronous orbit, spaced 120 degrees apart, so that they could cover all continents. He could not go into detail about how these relay satellites could be put into that orbit, since the largest rocket then in existence was the V-2, which could only climb to 100 miles. He also could not say how large these orbital relay stations would have to be, but he could show that they would be considerably cheaper than a system of relay towers that covered the same area on the ground.

For a number of years the idea proposed by Clarke simply "was around," something radio engineers might think about during an idle weekend. Much later, when there were communications satellites in orbit, the Franklin Institute in Philadelphia awarded a gold medal to Arthur C. Clarke for having pointed the way.

Clarke's article was one side of the story.

The other side was that a number of people privately wondered how one could make a satellite both light in weight and large in size so that it would be easily visible. One afternoon in 1952 or 1953 Wernher von Braun told me about an idea of his which he called the American Star. Rockets that could carry any weight worth mentioning into orbit did not yet exist, but a rocket that might be able to orbit something weighing only a few pounds was likely to be built soon. These few pounds, in von Braun's idea, could be a bottle holding plastic foam of some kind. When in orbit the valve would be opened by a timing device—a receiver for radio commands would have represented extra weight—

and the foam would come out. It would form a large sphere in orbit, consisting of millions and millions of foam bubbles. Because it was foam it would look white. It would also be large, though one could not even guess how large. With a little luck, the American Star would look brighter than the planet Venus at its brightest. To make it visible to practically everybody on earth, Wernher von Braun wanted to put the American Star into an orbit with an inclination of 66½ degrees so that it would be vertically overhead for every place between 66½ degrees northern latitude and 66½ degrees southern latitude. There would be no place on earth from which it could not be seen.

The only uncertain element in the scheme was that nobody could tell how such foam would behave in space. Personally, I wondered whether the pressure-packaged foam, expanding into the vacuum of space, might not expand so rapidly that it would tear the "star" apart. I still don't know whether this worry was justified or not, but I began to speak, in many lectures, about a balloon satellite. Make a large balloon of a plastic film, I suggested, and inflate it in orbit.* Use a plastic that can be colored yellow for distinctiveness and is not elastic, or has only a very small degree of elasticity. A balloon satellite of a non-elastic plastic, I said, would still keep its shape, even if punctured by a tiny meteorite. If the balloon were punctured, the air would escape, of course, but since the outside pressure is zero, the balloon would not collapse.

Somewhere inside NASA the two ideas, the lightweight balloon satellite and the orbiting radio relay began to fuse.

_____
* I had in mind that a very small carbon dioxide cartridge, of the type one uses to make soda at home, would do the inflating. Now we know that no device of any kind is needed; the little air that is left in the folds of even a very tightly packed balloon is fully sufficient to inflate it in space.

One did not need the amplifiers Clarke had been talking about; all one needed was a reflector for radio waves. An orbiting balloon would be a reflector.

Thus the idea of Echo was born; its name was obvious, because it would produce a radio echo. Echo was made of Mylar, covered with an ultra-thin film of aluminum. It had a diameter of 100 feet. And on August 12, 1960, it was put into a nearly circular orbit (perigee at 1018 miles, apogee at 1160 miles) with an inclination of 47.3 degrees of arc to the equator. Echo not only worked beautifully as a radio and even television reflector, it also became the American Star. Many millions of people all over the globe watched the point of light moving across the sky for years.

Echo was the first satellite that was light enough and large enough to be visibly influenced by the radiation pressure of the sun. Its orbit changed considerably from time to time. Of course it was punctured by micrometeorites; it seems to have acquired a lopsided shape. Still, it was easily visible, and it stayed in orbit for a long time. A solid satellite in the orbit of Echo would still be there; light-weight Echo, responding to radiation pressure, finally re-entered the atmosphere on May 24, 1968.

Echo was a "passive" communications satellite, just a reflector. The advantage of such passive satellites is that they don't cost much. The disadvantage is that the receiving equipment on the ground has to be very sensitive, because the balloon reflects only a very small percentage of the radio waves that come up from the ground. An active communications satellite, one that receives the signal and re-broadcasts it, is more complicated and more expensive, but the ground instrumentation does not need to be so sensitive.

The first satellite of this type was Courier I, launched

October 4, 1960, on the third anniversary of Sputnik I. It mainly had the purpose to see whether it worked.

The first commercial communications satellite was Telstar I, launched July 10, 1962. It was so successful that it convinced everybody who had an interest in such matters at all that communications satellites were not only nice to have in an emergency, but were the future of communications. Telstar I was not in a very large orbit (perigee at 593 miles, apogee at 3503 miles), and that fact caused a number of debates among the experts. Was it better to have a number of communications satellites in low orbits, or just a few of them in the synchronous orbit?

Experience proved that a satellite in the synchronous orbit was superior. Arthur C. Clarke's early suggestion turned out to be the best.

But we are not quite at the end of the story yet.

Communications satellites are not only useful for businessmen, news reporters, and bank managers; they are useful to the military, too. So there are also military communications satellites in orbit.

It is logical that all military thinking has to include a large number of pessimistic thoughts. A businessman only has to worry about possible reverses, wrong speculations, market slumps. A military man has to take enemy action into account. It is impossible to hide a satellite; anybody with the necessary equipment can track it. It might be possible to hide the function of a satellite, but since the functions of most satellites are known, an enemy can easily make a list of the relatively few of which the function is not known.

Having reasoned up to that point, the military planner has to find out whether an enemy could destroy a military communications satellite of the other side. To "destroy," in this case, does not necessarily mean that the satellite is smashed to bits or is knocked out of its orbit. It is enough to damage it to the point where it does not function any more. If one does not know what an enemy might be able to do, it is best to try to do it to oneself. A few years ago the Air Force revealed that a system for destroying satellites had been developed. Very likely, target satellites were orbited for just this purpose.

Since it had been proved that it could be done, one had to assume that "the enemy" (whoever that might be) could also do it. Was there no way of producing a communications satellite that could not be harmed?

Some Air Force scientists thought they had an answer, and that answer was called Project West Ford. The idea was to embed hundreds of thousands of short and thin copper wires into a substance that would slowly evaporate in space. With this package in orbit, the copper wires would be released slowly, a few at a time, and would form a ring around the earth. This ring of copper wires would be a fine reflector for radio waves; it would be a communications satellite that could not be damaged in any manner.

When Project West Ford was announced, there were protests from a great many scientists, especially from astronomers, and most especially from radio astronomers, who were afraid that the "needles" would interfere with their work. The Air Force pointed out in reply that the sun's radiation pressure would slowly force the copper wires into the atmosphere and it was estimated that in seven years every one of them would have re-entered. The test of a communications device that could not be damaged would, therefore, interfere with astronomical work only temporarily. Of course, the Air Force did not wish to maintain such a ring of copper needles all the time; it just wanted to know whether it would be useful in case of need.

The canister containing the "needles" was placed into

orbit, in spite of scientific opposition. Nothing happened. The canister orbited in one piece and finally re-entered; the needles had never been released.

In spite of continuous protests, the Air Force repeated the experiment, and this time the needles did spread out along the orbit. They did not interfere with astronomy, they did not cause trouble for radio astronomers, and they also did not produce a useful reflector in space for military communications.

After that, the Air Force returned to the orbiting of normal communications satellites. The possibility of enemy counteraction still exists, of course. But meanwhile they work.

# CHAPTER VIII

# The Manned Satellites

EVERYBODY is agreed that later historians will say that the release of atomic energy and space travel were the two major accomplishments of the twentieth century. Yet it is interesting to recall how the roads toward these accomplishments varied.

The "radio-chemists," as the explorers of the atom called themselves before the Second World War, did not have any consistent theory to go by, for they were working hard in their laboratories to create such a theory. They devised experiments which would chip off little bits of the nucleus of an atom. But the key fact on which to build the theory, namely, that a uranium atom might break into two roughly equal halves, still remained to be discovered. When Enrico Fermi in Italy accidentally succeeded in splitting the uranium atom, he thought that he had found (or made) elements heavier than uranium with chemical characteristics similar to platinum. Otto Hahn in Berlin repeated the experiment and could finally prove that no heavy elements had been produced. But he did not know just what had been going on. Dr. Lise Meitner, Hahn's collaborator for many years, proved some time later that a uranium nucleus must have broken into two large and several smaller pieces.

The key that unlocked the door that led to atomic energy had finally been found.

While the atomic physicists had to feel their way from experiment to experiment, the "space travelers" began with an almost complete theory and mapped out many years in advance what they had to do to go into space. In fact, they gave such detailed descriptions of the things that would have to be done that they were sometimes ridiculed for their self-assurance. But in outline their plan was simple: First, small experimental rockets would have to be built. These rockets would gradually grow larger, until they were large enough to carry a man above the atmosphere. Manned space flight would begin with nearly vertical ascents to 100 and then to 300 or even 500 miles. Orbital flight would be next. Then a space station in orbit around the earth would be built. And then, with the space station as an assembly base for still bigger ships, flights to the moon and to the neighboring planets could be made.

Since the progression from small to large rockets, to manned orbital flight, and to the construction of a space station was logical, it should not be surprising that the Russians had the same scheme in mind.

And up to manned orbital flight the original scheme (with the addition of unmanned artificial satellites) was followed faithfully. The Russians, if you take them at their word, are still following the scheme, while the United States devoted several years to an additional project, known as Project Apollo.

So far, no nation except the United States and the Soviet Union have sent men into space, and the two nations that did were, of course, in competition with each other. However, it would be confusing to the reader if one tried to tell the total effort in strictly chronological order. It is easier to tell what the Russians did and what the Americans did in separate accounts. Since the Russians were ahead at first, let's begin with them.

As has been told, the Sputnik series of artificial satellites led to the first Russian manned flight in a straight line: Sputnik X was orbited March 25, 1961, and de-orbited the next day. Yuri Gagarin went into orbit in Vostok I on April 12, 1961. Major Gherman Stepanovitch Titov was the second man to orbit the earth; the date was August 6, 1961. He stayed in orbit for 25 hours and 18 minutes and completed 17 orbits around the earth. The reason for making the flight so long was certainly medical; the Russian doctors wanted to know whether a man could sleep while in orbit, and how his body would function in other respects in prolonged weightlessness.

There was no additional manned flight by the Soviets in 1961, and not even an unmanned Soviet satellite. The next Soviet satellite after Sputnik X was Kosmos I, orbited on March 16, 1962. Since then, there have been hundreds of Kosmos satellites and only a very few with other names.

The third Soviet manned flight did not take place until August 11, 1962, when Colonel Andrian Gregoryevitch Nikolayeff took Vostok III into orbit for a 64-orbit flight. On the next day Colonel Pavel Romanovitch Popovitch took off in Vostok IV for 48 orbits. Of course, the two spaceships were in radio contact with each other, but we do not know whether they tried to come close together; if they did try, they did not succeed.

Again there was a long pause of nearly a year in the Russian manned flight program. Because of the long pause, journalists who love sensation and are not deterred by ethics invented stories of catastrophe. One Italian news agency sent out a story of two dead Russian cosmonauts in orbit around the earth. The agency had the bad luck to

**113**

pick a time when there was nothing in orbit—either Russian or American—that was large enough to hold even one man. Another European agency sent out a story that 140 Russian scientists and generals were killed when a rocket exploded on the launch pad. By that time the Russians must have fired more than a thousand large rockets and must have worked out a safety procedure which could not have been violated by the Chief of State himself. When you have a fully fueled rocket on the pad, everybody is either under cover with lots of concrete overhead, or else so far away that an explosion would only be an interesting spectacle, not a danger.

In the Soviet Union a man is given the title Cosmonaut only after he has been in space; those who have only been through training are called candidates, and the names of candidates are not made public. Because of this system, the Russians could spring a little surprise with the next two Vostok flights: One of the cosmonauts was a pretty woman. Vostok V was piloted by Lieutenant Colonel Valery Fyodorovitch Bykovsky, who took off on June 14, 1963. Vostok VI took off on June 16, with Valentina Vladimirovna Tereshkova on board. Vostok V went through 81 orbits around the earth, Vostok VI through 48.*

Again there followed a long pause—fifteen months—but this time one could see a reason for it. The next two flights were made by a new type of spaceship called Voskhod which, being heavier than the first type, needed a new and heavier carrier rocket. Both must have taken time to be developed and tested; some of the prototypes of the Voskhod were probably orbited in the series of Kosmos satellites.

Voskhod I went into space on October 12, 1964, and presented the world with two innovations. It was the first

* Valentina Tereshkova later married Colonel Nikolayeff of Vostok III.

114

spacecraft to carry more than one person; it carried three. And only the commander, Colonel Vladimir Mihailovitch Komarov, wore a spacesuit; the other two men did not. They were Boris Borisovitch Yegorov, M.D., a civilian, and Konstantin Petrovitch Feoktistov, a scientist and engineer, also a civilian. The flight plan called for 16 orbits, and during the 16th orbit Komarov pleaded for permission to keep going, since everything went so well. But ground control on the Soviet side is as stern as ground control on the American side—if not more so—and simply ordered him to land according to plan. He did.

Voskhod II, on March 18, 1965, carried only two men: Colonel Pavel Ivanovitch Belyayev and Lieutenant Colonel Alexei Arkhipovitch Leonov. During the flight both men wore spacesuits, and in flight they opened the escape hatch and Leonov went outside, for a period of about 20 minutes. For the first time in history, men were protected against the space environment by their suits only. After his return Leonov, who is a good amateur artist, made drawings showing how he thinks he would have looked to an observer in another ship nearby. (Fig. 6) The flight lasted for 17 orbits.

Another long pause followed; during that pause the American Gemini Program racked up success after success. It so happens that there never was an American and a Russian manned spacecraft in orbit at the same time. Since NASA always announces flights weeks ahead, and since it had also announced that there would be a total of ten manned flights in the Gemini Program, the Russians apparently waited until they could be sure to have the sky to themselves.

The next Russian flight again involved a new spaceship, named Soyuz. Though the Soyuz is believed to have room for five men, there was only a single cosmonaut in the first Soyuz when it took off on April 23, 1967. The cosmonaut

Fig. 6. Colonel Leonov's drawing of his own "space walk."

was Colonel Komarov of Voskhod I. Unfortunately, the flight ended in catastrophe. After 17 orbits, Colonel Komarov re-entered and, at an altitude of about 23,000 feet, released his parachute. But the lines fouled and the ship crashed, killing Komarov.

During the year following Komarov's crash the Soviets launched several very large "Kosmos" satellies, no doubt changed versions of Soyuz I. Moreover, they launched over a dozen smaller Kosmos satellites that were left in orbit for only one day—presumably satellites testing new parachute systems.

Soyuz II was sent into orbit on October 25, 1968, but unmanned. The next day Soyuz III was orbited, with only one man, cosmonaut Georgi Beregovoi, inside. Beregovoi maneuvered his craft to the vicinity of Soyuz II, "making rendezvous." This is the term used when a manned vessel in orbit closely approaches another orbiting object, manned or unmanned. Nobody has ever specified how close one has to be to have accomplished rendezvous; but everybody is agreed that the job would be considered accomplished if the manned vehicle is close enough to read an inscription on the other without using glasses. Beregovoi made rendezvous repeatedly; whether he also accomplished a docking (physical contact with the other vessel) has not been disclosed by the Russians. The unmanned Soyuz II was de-orbited on October 28, 1968; Beregovoi stayed in orbit with Soyuz III for another two days and re-entered after his 68th orbit.

In January 1969, three weeks after Apollo 8 had circled the moon, the Soviet cosmonauts produced *their* masterpiece. Soyuz IV took off from the Russian space port of Baikonur (the Russians call it a Kosmodrome) with cosmonaut Vladimir Aleksandrovitch Shatalov aboard. Twenty-four hours later, when Soyuz V took off, Shatalov was overhead and said "Amur is watching" from orbit—Amur being his nickname. Command pilot of Soyuz V was Lieutenant Colonel Boris Volynov; with him were Lieutenant Colonel Yevgeni Khrunov and Alexei Yeliseyev, a civilian.

On the following day, over the Pacific Ocean, when Soyuz IV was in its 34th orbit and Soyuz V in its 18th, Khrunov and Yeliseyev left their vessel, stayed outside it for about an hour, and then entered Soyuz IV. Shatalov landed his Soyuz IV, now with three men in it, on January 17, near Karaganda in Kazakhstan. Soyuz V, now piloted by Volynov only, followed Soyuz IV 25 hours later.

The next big job, the Russians said a few weeks later, is to build a space station.

We can be certain that the Russians will first build one that is fairly small. What its shape is likely to be nobody except a small group of Russian planners knows—and they may be undecided themselves. But a likely shape for an early space station is that of a dumbbell: two more or less spherical cabins connected by a hollow shaft, with an airlock in the middle. The whole station would rotate around the center marked by the airlock. This rotation would produce a kind of pseudo-gravity in the cabins by way of the centrifugal effect. We now know that weightlessness can be accepted by trained men for rather long periods, but it is simply more convenient when things weigh something and fall to the floor when dropped, instead of floating around in the cabin.

The shape of the large space station to come has been definite for quite a number of years. The basic idea, a rotating wheel with crew accommodations in the wheel's rim, was developed by the retired Austrian army officer Captain Potočnik some time between 1925 and 1928. It is no longer possible to find out when he worked on it; he published his design in 1928 (writing under the name of Hermann Noordung) and died soon after the publication of his book.

Reading the book now, forty years after its publication, one can see that Potočnik made some mistakes. He wanted to place his space station in the synchronous orbit to make it easy to find. But a distance of 22,300 miles is inconveniently far from the ground, and observation of things on the ground from that distance would be difficult. Some other mistakes are due to the fact that he was worried that the occupants of the space station might freeze to death, unless the station was well heated by the sun.

By now the main worry would be that it might get too warm in the space station, but at the time Potočnik wrote it was customary to talk of the "cold of space." For some reason, it took a long time until it was generally realized that space cannot have any temperature at all. A rock can be hot or cold, water can be hot or cold, and the same goes for air, but it is always matter that is either hot or cold. A vacuum, however, means that matter is absent, hence a vacuum can be neither hot nor cold.

But the wheel shape, first published in 1928, persisted in the thinking of space planners. It is fine for the purpose of providing a home in space for people who will be there for at least several weeks and possibly several months. It also is easy to construct.

Many years after the publication of "Hermann Noordung's" book, Wernher von Braun, when at Fort Bliss, used his spare time to work out an expedition to Mars. He just wanted to see what rocket engineering had to do before such an expedition became possible. And he found out very soon that an expedition to Mars could be undertaken only if a space station were put into orbit first. It would have to be there to serve as a base for assembling the ships that would go to Mars and for fueling them. There is a great advantage to such assembly in orbit. The ships can have any shape that engineering reasoning dictates, since they do not have to ascend into orbit from the surface and go through our atmosphere.

Another advantage is the following: Let us assume that the space station orbits the earth in a circular orbit 330 miles above sea level. It would be far enough from the ground so that its occupants could see a large portion of the earth at a glance. But it would be close enough so that fine detail could be seen. Its orbital period would be 95 minutes, and its velocity in orbit would be 4.7 miles per second. Everything that orbits with or near the station would, of course, have the same orbital velocity. To go to Mars a velocity of about 7 miles per second is needed. Since a ship assembled in space near the station would already have a velocity of 4.7 miles per second, it only has to provide another 2.3 miles per second to make the trip.

Wernher von Braun's space station, as described in *The*

*Mars Project,** would be wheel-shaped. While the original manuscript of *The Mars Project* was being printed, the design was refined in many respects for publication in a special issue of *Collier's* magazine (March 22, 1952), but the shape remained that of a wheel.

Originally, Wernher von Braun's main consideration had been the assembly of other spaceships in orbit near the station. But it soon turned out that the space station would be useful for many other functions, all of which could be called "surveillance." But it would not be military surveillance only. The space station could serve as a weather watch, it could be most helpful to the Iceberg Patrol, and it could spot lost aircraft or ships drifting helplessly. It could even assist in the search for natural resources. It would, in short, be something very useful to have.

But now we have to speak about the American space flight programs which could be considered preliminaries to the construction of the manned satellite, the space station.

The first program was Project Mercury.

It was to consist of six manned flights and as many unmanned flights as needed. Seven astronauts were selected from more than a hundred volunteers, all of them qualified Air Force and Navy pilots. The seven were, in alphabetical order: M. Scott Carpenter, L. Gordon Cooper, John H. Glenn, Virgil I. Grissom, Walter H. Schirra, Alan B. Shepard, and Donald K. Slayton. Not all of them were to go into orbit. Unlike the Russian program that proceeded from orbital flights by animals directly to a manned flight, the orbital flights of Project Mercury were to be preceded by so-called sub-orbital flights. The orbital flights would require the lifting power of the Atlas rocket, while the smaller Redstone rocket could be used for sub-orbital

* German edition 1952, English edition 1953.

**120**

flights. Hence the program had two phases, called MR for Mercury/Redstone and MA for Mercury/Atlas.

Even the sub-orbital flights were preceded by an animal experiment. MR-2, fired January 31, 1961 (MR-1 had been a test of the capsule) carried a chimpanzee named Ham over a distance of 422 miles. The peak of this flight was 157 miles above the Atlantic.

MR-3 followed on May 5, 1961, but this time there was a man aboard—astronaut Alan B. Shepard. The sub-orbital flight lasted for 15 minutes and 28 seconds, the range was 303 miles, and the peak was 116.5 miles up. The medical examination and questioning Shepard had to undergo afterwards lasted twenty-four times as long as the whole flight; the doctors wanted to make sure that they did not miss anything. They were especially anxious about the 5 minutes and 16 seconds of weightlessness during the flight; this was then a novel experience.

MR-4 was fired on July 26, 1961, with astronaut Virgil I. Grissom in the capsule. The flight was a repeat of MR-3, the peak was 2 miles higher, and the range 1 mile shorter. But while the helicopters hovered overhead, the escape hatch of the floating capsule suddenly opened and the capsule began to fill with sea water. Grissom escaped through the open hatch and was rescued by another helicopter; the capsule was too heavy for a helicopter to carry, being full of water, and had to be abandoned.

After MR-4 the project moved into the MA phase. Again there were some unmanned flights, with MA-4 orbiting an instrumented dummy. MA-5, on November 29, 1961, carried a chimpanzee named Enos. It was supposed to orbit the earth three times, but in the second hour of the flight something failed to work properly and Enos was de-orbited, and rescued, after 2 orbits.

**121**

On February 20, 1962, after several postponements, MA-6 rose into the sky, carrying Lieutenant Colonel John H. Glenn. Glenn performed 3 orbits, re-entered and splashed down after 4 hours 55 minutes and 23 seconds, counting from lift-off. The first American manned orbital flight had gone well, but Glenn made a few recommendations afterwards. He said that there were too many things aboard that were not really needed, and some of the superfluous equipment was removed.

MA-7, with M. Scott Carpenter aboard, took off on May 24, 1962, also for 3 orbits. The whole flight went well, except that Carpenter's capsule overshot the splash-down point and it took some time until he was located in the ocean; fortunately, the weather in the area was perfect. MA-8, with Walter H. Schirra inside, took off on October 3, 1962, for a 6-orbit flight. Of all the flights in the Mercury program, Schirra's flight went farthest away from the earth: his apogee was at 175.8 miles. The perigee was at an even 100 miles. The Mercury program ended with the first American long-duration flight: 34 hours and 20 minutes, during which time 22½ orbits were flown. Takeoff was on May 15, 1963, and L. Gordon Cooper was the pilot of MA-9. While he was still in orbit, the next manned-space-flight program was already under discussion.

The new spacecraft was to hold two astronauts; logically it was called Project Gemini, "the twins." Of course, the new spacecraft would be considerably heavier than the Mercury capsules, and it would need a more powerful rocket. That point presented a problem for some time. The rocket that could carry the Gemini spacecraft would have to be the Air Force's Titan II, an intercontinental missile. But Titan II suffered from something that was called the Pogo Effect, named after the Pogo stick. It tended to shake somewhat while climbing. That did not matter as long as the rocket was used as a missile, but with people riding in its nose the story was different.

While one group of scientists, engineers, and technicians developed the Gemini spacecraft, another group went to work on the Titan II with the objective of ridding it of the Pogo Effect. Both groups were successful, and on April 8, 1964, GT-I (GT for Gemini/Titan) took off. It only orbited an empty (but weighted) capsule which was left in orbit for 64 revolutions around the earth. GT-II, on January 19, 1965, only made a long sub-orbital flight with a range of 2127 miles. It had the purpose of testing the spacecraft once more, especially its re-entry performance, and also provided an exercise for the rescue forces.

Since the United States, by then, already had a number of astronauts with experience in space, the idea was to have one experienced man and one novice on every flight, as far as that could be done. That way, the number of experienced astronauts would be increased rapidly.

The list of the ten manned flights of the Gemini Program is shown on the next page.

The table shows that the program was carried out in about one and a half years. The table also shows that failures were avoided; there was one, but it did not result in disaster. However, the table cannot show everything that was done.

GT-III was a short flight, mainly to see how the spacecraft would behave when manned. A few orbit changes, pre-planned, were made during the flight. GT-IV had three objectives: long duration, rendezvous with the orbiting upper stage of the Titan rocket, and the first American spacewalk. The latter, performed by White, came off very well; White crossed the width of the United States outside the spacecraft. The rendezvous with the orbiting rocket stage had to be abandoned, the two vehicles being too far

| Number | Launch date | Number of orbits flown | Duration (liftoff-to splash-down) | Command Pilot Co-Pilot |
|---|---|---|---|---|
| GT-III | Mar. 23, 1965 | 3 | 4 hr. 54 min. | Virgil I. Grissom<br>John W. Young |
| GT-IV | June 3, 1965 | 66 | 4 d. 1 hr. 59 min. | James A. McDivitt<br>Edward H. White II |
| GT-V | Aug. 21, 1965 | 120 | 7 d. 22 hr. 59 min. | L. Gordon Cooper<br>Charles P. Conrad |
| GT-VII | Dec. 4, 1965 | 206 | 13 d. 18 hr. 35 min. | Frank Borman<br>James A. Lovell |
| GT-VI | Dec. 15, 1965 | 16 | 1 d. 1 hr. 52 min. | Walter M. Schirra<br>Thomas P. Stafford |
| GT-VIII | Mar. 16, 1966 | 7 | 10 hr. 42 min. | Neil A. Armstrong<br>David R. Scott |
| GT-IX | June 3, 1966 | 46 | 3 d. 0 hr. 21 min. | Thomas P. Stafford<br>Eugene A. Cernan |
| GT-X | July 18, 1966 | 43 | 2 d. 22 hr. 47 min. | John W. Young<br>Michael Collins |
| GT-XI | Sept. 12, 1966 | 44 | 2 d. 23 hr. 17 min. | Charles P. Conrad<br>Richard F. Gordon |
| GT-XII | Nov. 11, 1966 | 59 | 3 d. 22 hr. 36 min. | James A. Lovell<br>Edwin E. Aldrin |

apart. The long duration was achieved, of course, but the astronauts slept very little; the waking member just could not avoid disturbing the sleeping member in the cramped space.

The solution for later long-duration flights was simple: Both astronauts went to sleep at the same time; there is, after all, not yet any need for "standing watch" in space.

GT-V was to double the duration of GT-IV, and did. But the mission turned into a very quiet flight because of a power failure. It was the first time that the fairly new fuel cells were to be tested in space. A fuel cell burns hydrogen with oxygen in such a manner that an electric current is generated; the only by-product is water. In a fuel-cell installation on the ground the two gases can be in pressure bottles; for use in flight the gases must be liquid to eliminate the high weight of steel bottles. But that means that they must be evaporated by heat, and the heat is furnished by a glow wire, such as is used in restaurants to keep coffeepots hot. Somewhere a contact must have been broken, for the glow wire did not glow. It was decided to go on without power from the fuel cell, and after a few days the fuel cell began to work at a very low level; heat from the spacecraft helped to evaporate some of the liquid gases.

GT-VI had a peculiar fate. It was to make rendezvous in orbit with an Agena rocket that was carried into space by an Atlas. The Atlas took off 101 minutes before the scheduled takeoff of GT-VI. But there were no signals from the Agena, and radar could not find it. One had to assume that it had exploded on ignition; the takeoff of GT-VI was canceled. GT-VI was supposed to wait for another Agena. But meanwhile GT-VII was ready, and did take off. The plan was changed quickly; GT-VI would take off and make rendezvous with the orbiting GT-VII. In the early afternoon of December 15, 1965, the two spacecraft approached each other closely. The astronauts estimated that they were only 10 feet apart; measurements of the photographs taken during the approach showed that the actual closest distance had been 2 or 3 feet. GT-VI then flew around GT-VII; after some time GT-VI pulled away and made ready for re-entry. GT-VII stayed in orbit; it was the first American flight where the astronauts took their spacesuits off inside the spacecraft for a long time.

GT-VIII was the only flight where there was a mishap that could have had serious consequences. GT-VIII was to make rendezvous and dock with an orbiting Agena. During the 5th revolution after takeoff, the spacecraft did make

**125**

rendezvous and docked. Forty minutes later the two joined vessels began to roll and pitch. It was thought that the Agena was at fault and there was danger in the fact that the Agena's fuel tanks were still half-full. Astronaut Armstrong disconnected his spacecraft as fast as he could and, after consultation with ground control, re-entered, made a perfect splashdown, and was promptly recovered. It then turned out that a thruster on the Gemini spacecraft had malfunctioned; it kept burning until the whole system was disconnected.

GT-IX also had a rendezvous mission, which was carried out, but the docking could not be carried out because the target device had failed to jettison its nose cone. The co-pilot spent about two hours outside the capsule, the longest period at the time.

GT-X made two rendezvous and one docking. First it made rendezvous and docked with the Agena rocket that had been put into orbit for this purpose. After docking, the Gemini spacecraft, using the fuel left in the Agena, extended its orbit to an apogee of 474 miles, higher than any astronaut or cosmonaut had gone before. The two vehicles remained docked for nearly 40 hours, then command pilot Young disconnected and went after the Agena left in orbit from GT-VIII. He made a close rendezvous but did not try docking, because his supply of maneuvering fuel was low by then. But co-pilot Collins went outside and, using a backpack propulsion unit, reached the Agena and stayed with it for 27 minutes.

GT-XI docked with the Agena rocket fired about two hours ahead of its own takeoff precisely 94 minutes after lift-off and used the Agena fuel to extend the orbit to an apogee of 850 miles, almost twice as far as Gemini X. On the last Gemini flight the co-pilot had to work much harder than the command pilot; co-pilot Aldrin spent a total of

126

5½ hours outside the spacecraft; the longest consecutive period was slightly more than two hours. Of course, the astronauts of Gemini XII also made rendezvous with an Agena rocket, but they were told not to try to use the Agena's fuel, for the fuel pump in the Agena was not trustworthy.

While the Gemini Program was running its course, the space flight center in Huntsville, Alabama, put the first large United States rocket that was not a missile through a test-flight program. This was the Saturn, bigger than anything that had ever taken off from a launch pad, bigger, in fact, than a missile had a right to be. The Saturn, in spite of all its size and impressiveness, was only a test rocket, forerunner of still larger rockets to come. There were ten test flights; they were ten successes. Then the Saturn IB came and made three test flights, also three successes.

In the meantime another novel rocket was tested, the Centaur.* Oberth had said for the first time in 1923 that the upper stage of a large rocket should be fueled by liquid hydrogen and liquid oxygen; a brave statement at a time when liquid hydrogen was something you sometimes had in a laboratory, and then only one or two ounces of it. The Centaur was the liquid-hydrogen rocket predicted by Oberth. There had been some problems on the test stand, but once it flew, it flew well.

The success of the Centaur then enabled the designers to develop the two upper stages of the Saturn V rocket which also are hydrogen/oxygen rockets.

In December 1966 one could hope that the first Saturn V rocket would make its first test flight about a year later. That hope was fulfilled, but in the meantime there was

---

* It is somewhat confusing that there is also a French rocket called *Centaure,* but the French rocket is only a solid-fuel, high-altitude research rocket.

tragedy. The command module of the Apollo spacecraft was to make its first manned orbital flight late in February 1967, to be carried into orbit by a Saturn IB. The three astronauts selected were Virgil I. Grissom, veteran of MR-IV and GT-III, Edward H. White, first "space walker" of GT-IV, and Roger B. Chaffee, who was eager for his first orbital flight. There was to be a routine test on January 27; in the program scheduled it was called "Apollo 204."

Suddenly there was a fire in the spacecraft that was perched on top of the (unfueled) Saturn IB. The hatch cover, which had been designed to hold tight, was too tight; it took the technicians on the outside six minutes to open it. By that time it was more than five minutes too late; the three astronauts were dead.

Hundreds of changes, some large (like a new escape hatch) and some small (different fabrics for upholstery and a different kind of insulation for the wiring) had to be made in the command module before it could be called safe.

In the meantime, the first Saturn V rocket was readied and scheduled to take off on November 9, 1967, at 7 A.M. Eastern Standard Time. It was the biggest and noisiest rocket I have ever seen. Taking off about 1.4 seconds behind schedule, it shook the ground for thousands of feet around the launch pad. It passed through a thin cloud layer and burned a large hole into it through which it could be seen. Its official designation was "Apollo 4," but it is no longer the biggest and noisiest rocket I have seen, for in the meantime I watched Apollo 8 take off for the moon. Since this was the same type of rocket, it was just as big and just as noisy, but it did not have to burn its way through a cloud layer, for there were no clouds in the sky.

One of the experiments of Apollo 4 was to carry the command module far out into space and make it re-enter with a velocity as if it had come back from the moon. Splash-down was to be near Hawaii, and in the evening two events could be celebrated at the Cape: the successful splash-down and recovery of a still serviceable command module and the successful landing of lunar probe Surveyor VI on the moon.

During the year 1967 five lunar orbiters circled the moon, photographing its surface in order to find landing areas for the lunar landing. Simultaneously, seven Surveyors were sent to land on the moon for the same purpose. Of the five lunar orbiters five were successful; of the seven Surveyors five were successful.

But by the fall of 1968 the Apollo command module had only been tested unmanned; it had not yet been flown with astronauts inside. The first manned flight of the command module was Apollo 7, which splashed down at 7:10 A.M. (Eastern Daylight Time) on October 22, 1968, after 260 hours in space. The number of orbits flown was 163. Command pilot was Walter M. Schirra, veteran of MA-VIII and GT-VI, Donn F. Eisele, and R. Walter Cunningham; for the latter two it was the first flight. The flight of Apollo 7 was not supposed to establish any records, and it didn't. It was not the longest earth-orbital flight, nor was it the highest. But it was one that did everything so well that the astronauts not only accomplished all the missions in the flight plan but performed additional experiments that were conceived on the ground while they were in orbit. At one point ground control asked Schirra whether he wanted to go on to beat the 206-orbit record of GT-VII; Schirra declined.

When Apollo 7 returned, the testing of the ship that would go to the moon was not yet complete. Apollo 4 had tested the Saturn V rocket, the command module of the Apollo spacecraft, and the service module, the medium-sized rocket on which the command module depends for propulsion and maneuvering. But the whole test flight had been unmanned. Apollo 7 had tested the command module and the service module under human control. The rocket for Apollo 7 was a Saturn IB; not a Saturn V.

The next step was to send the service module and command module into space with the Apollo V rocket that had not yet been used to carry people. That was Apollo 8, and it was ready on December 21, 1968.

Takeoff was scheduled at 7:51 A.M., Eastern Standard Time.

Takeoff took place at 7:51 A.M.

The astronauts in the command module were Frank Borman and James A. Lovell, who had made the long-duration flight of GT-VII together. The third man was William A. Anders, for whom this was the first flight.

At lift-off the weight was 6,218,558 pounds; what went into the parking orbit 119 miles from the ground still weighed 284,000 pounds. That was the combined weight of the S-IVB (the Saturn's top stage), the Instrument Section, the service module, and the command module. The spacecraft orbited the earth 1½ times, then the S-IVB pushed the whole into the "moon corridor," the flight path to the moon. When the necessary velocity was reached, the S-IVB was separated from the Apollo spacecraft, then re-ignited by remote command to go into a different flight path to the moon. This flight path was calculated to put the rocket stage into such a position relative to the moon that the moon's gravitational field would deflect it into an orbit around the sun.

What happened to the spacecraft itself has been seen by virtually everybody who owns a TV set. The first telecast from the command module came on December 22, when the spacecraft was about halfway to the moon. On December 24 the spacecraft was near the moon, and the rocket engine of the service module reduced the speed, so that the moon's gravitational field could "capture" the spacecraft. The orbit would have been elliptical, but more burns "circularized" it, so that the spacecraft settled in an orbit about 70 miles from the lunar surface.

Then 10 orbits around the moon were flown; the total time consumed by this maneuver was 20 hours. Thanks to TV, the people on earth could see the moon as it looked to the astronauts. On December 25 the engine of the service module fired once more, this time putting the spacecraft into the return orbit to earth. The return path was so precise that course corrections that had been scheduled were found to be unnecessary. On December 27, shortly before re-entry, the command module was separated from the service module. The command module re-entered and splashed down in the Pacific to the south of Hawaii, where the carrier U.S.S. *Yorktown* was waiting. Splash-down was 16,500 feet from the carrier; the three astronauts were all healthy and triumphant.

Apollo 9 was to test the one component of the Apollo mooncraft that had not been tested in space yet, the LM (which came to be known as "spider" in the course of the test flight), which is the vehicle that will touch down on the lunar surface. But very small things can cause big delays, the very small things in this case being the virus of the common cold. A day before the scheduled takeoff the astronauts came down with ordinary colds like anybody else. They were James A. McDivitt, who had flown in GT-IV; David R. Scott, who had been co-pilot to Neil Armstrong in GT-VIII (which almost went wrong); and Russell L. Schweickart, for whom this was the first flight. The delay caused by the cold virus lasted three days.

Apollo 9 took off on March 3, 1969, for an earth-orbiting

10-day mission. On the second day of the mission there was concern that it might have to be cut short. Schweickart, all of a sudden, had vomiting spells, which the medical men frankly stated they could not explain, even after they had examined Schweickart after his return. Fortunately, there was no need to shorten the mission; Schweickart recovered and was able to carry out his assignments as they had been planned, though not precisely on schedule.

The landing module was thoroughly tested, and its two parts are still orbiting. One of them, the lower portion of the LM, is likely to re-enter within a year; the upper portion of the LM will stay in orbit for about 20 years. Inside it are several expensive cameras and a TV camera which had to be left there in order to reduce the weight of the command module. They may still be recovered.

While NASA was busy with the Apollo program, the concept of the space station was not completely neglected. President Johnson had given a preliminary project to the Air Force; it is called MOL, for Manned Orbiting Laboratory.

The purpose is to have something in orbit that provides ample working space for astronauts. The MOL will be cylindrical in shape, with a diameter of 10 or 12 feet and a length of 40 feet. At one end there will be an airlock, made to fit the bottom of a Gemini spacecraft. The astronauts will fly a Gemini craft to the orbiting MOL, dock it, and enter the MOL through a hatch in the heat shield of the Gemini vehicle. Then, after completion of the mission, they will return to the Gemini and re-enter and splash down in the normal manner, leaving the MOL in orbit for the next group of visitors.

This planned procedure raised two questions. One was whether a heat shield with a hatch cover in it will still protest astronauts during re-entry. The other was whether a rocket balancing the 40-foot MOL on its nose would be stable during takeoff. The MOL would be light enough to be flown into orbit in one piece. But if it were too long to be carried in one piece, it would have to be assembled in orbit. This would be good practice, but would also be a complication one would avoid, if possible.

The way to find out was to try it, and the Air Force did, on November 3, 1966. A Titan IIIC rocket was used. Of course there was no MOL yet, so a 40-foot fuel tank substituted for one. And an old Gemini capsule with a 24-inch circular hatch in its heat shield was put on top of that, making a payload 49 feet tall. Since the Titan IIIC could carry more weight than that payload, three satellites were added.

The test was a success in every respect. The rocket was perfectly stable in spite of the tall payload; the substitute MOL and the three satellites were placed into four different orbits; and the Gemini capsule made a splash-down 5500 miles from the takeoff site. It was recovered and found to be re-usable.*

There are two big projects in the future.

One is a permanent base on the moon.

The other is the manned satellite that is called the space station.

* This capsule had made its first spaceflight under the designation GT-III. It is the only manned space capsule that has been flown twice, even though virtually all of them were re-usable.

# Glossary of Satellite Names

| | |
|---|---|
| ALOUETTE | Canadian research satellites; the word is French for "skylark." Also called "topside sounders." |
| ANNA | Letters stand for Army-Navy-NASA-Air Force; a satellite for the calibration of ground or shipboard equipment of all four agencies. |
| ARIEL | British-built research satellites. Name from Shakespeare, the "airy spirit" of *The Tempest*. |
| ATS | The letters stand for Application Technology Satellite, indicating that satellites so designated are not experimental. |
| AURORA | See ESRO. |
| BIOSATELLITE | An American research satellite, carrying small life forms, both animal and vegetable, which were exposed to cosmic rays for examination of the life forms. |

**135**

| | |
|---|---|
| CENTAUR | This is actually the name of a rocket, used as upper stage for an Atlas rocket. Its fuels are liquid hydrogen and liquid oxygen. In the course of testing, several Centaur rockets became satellites. |
| COMSAT | Abbreviation meaning communications satellites; also the name of the company using Comsats. A Milcomsat is, of course, a military communications satellite. |
| COURIER | Early communications satellite for testing purposes only. |
| D-1A | Designation of a French satellite which the French call *Diapason*. |
| DIADÈME | French research satellites; the name was given with reference to the fact that the launch rocket has the name *Diamant* (diamond), while the separate stages are named *Emeraude* (emerald) and *Rubis* (ruby). |
| DISCOVERER | U.S. Air Force satellites with orbits of high inclination. They were used for the first de-orbiting experiments. |
| EARLY BIRD | Name of one of the Comsats in the synchronous orbit. |
| ECHO | American "passive" communications satellite which reflected radio signals as a mountain may reflect sound waves— hence the name. |
| EGRS | The letters stand for Extra-Galactic Radiation Satellite. |

136

| | |
|---|---|
| ELEKTRON | Russian research satellites; the name presumably was given because one of their jobs was to measure the electron density in the Van Allen belts. |
| EROS | Proposed satellite for mapping natural resources, an extension of the U.S. Geological Survey. The letters stand for Earth Resources Observation Satellite; no connection with the asteroid named Eros. |
| ESRO | The name of the European Space Research Organization and of its satellites, which also have separate names. ESRO-I is named Aurora, ESRO-II is Iris. |
| ESSA | American research satellite. The letters stand for Environmental Sciences Service Administration, the government agency involved. |
| EXPLORER | Name self-explanatory; the early Explorers were in earth orbits with low inclination; later Explorers were put into very long orbits. |
| GEMINI | "Second generation" of American manned spacecraft, for two astronauts. Name was given with reference to the constellation Gemini, the Twins. The flights were designated GT for Gemini spacecraft and Titan, the launch rocket. |
| GGSE | The letters stand for Gravity Gradient Stabilization Experiment. The satellite carried a weight on a long boom, to see whether the earth's gravity could be used to stabilize the satellite. It worked. |

| | |
|---|---|
| GREB | The letters mean Galactic Radiation Energy Background, but since these satellites were used to monitor solar radiation, their synonym SOLRAD is more descriptive. They are piggyback satellites, weighing about 40 pounds. |
| HEOS | The letters stand for High Eccentricity Orbiting Satellite; it follows a very elongated orbit. |
| HITCHHIKER | As the name indicates, this is an experimental satellite launched with other spacecraft if an additional payload of about 180 pounds can be accommodated. |
| INTELSAT | Communications satellite belonging to the International Satellite Communications Consortium. |
| IRIS | See ESRO. |
| ISIS | Canadian-built research satellite; letters stand for International Satellite for Ionosphere Studies. |
| KOSMOS | Often spelled "Cosmos" in American lists. Russian research satellites of all types, ranging from prototypes of manned spacecraft to weather research and probably reconnaissance satellites. |
| LM | Pronounced *lem*, meaning Lunar Module; originally caled LEM for Lunar Excursion Module. The part of the Apollo spacecraft that lands on the moon. The flight of Apollo 9 put the two parts of an LM into satellite orbits around the earth. The lower part of the LM is |

called the Descent Module, the upper part the Ascent Module.

LOFTI            The letters stand for Low Frequency Trans-Ionospheric Satellite.

LUNA            Designation of Russian moon probes, without distinction between moon-orbiting and moon-landing devices. The word is the Russian name of the moon, pronounced *loo-NAH*, with the accent on the last syllable.

LUNAR ORBITER  American device for photographic mapping of the moon, done while orbiting the moon. All five of the series were successful.

LUNIK           Mistaken designation of Russian moon probes, term coined by American newspapermen in analogy with sputnik. Actually the Russians used the term Cosmic Rocket I, II, and III. Afterwards they adopted the name Luna for their moon probes and renamed the three Cosmic Rockets Luna I, II, and III.

MERCURY         First type of American manned spacecraft for one astronaut. Name was given with reference to Mercury, the "swift messenger" of the gods. Flights were designated MA for Mercury spacecraft and Atlas, the launch rocket.

MIDAS           American military satellite; letters stand for Missile Defense Alarm System.

MOLNIYA         Russian communication satellites; the name is pronounced *MOL-niya* with the accent on the first syllable. It means "lightning."

OAO

American satellite for astronomical research; the letters stand for Orbiting Astronomical Observatory.

OGO

American research satellite; letters stand for Orbiting Geophysical Observatory.

OSCAR

Small satellites launched with other payloads. Letters stand for Orbiting Satellite Carrying Amateur Radio.

OSO

American astronomical research satellite; the letters stand for Orbiting Solar Observatory.

OV-1, 2, 3

Air Force research satellites launched with other payload; the letters simply mean Orbiting Vehicle, while the number following the letters indicates the type.

PAGEOS

The letters stand for Passive Geodetic Earch Orbiting Satellite. They are balloon-type satellites that must be observed, since they carry no transmitters. The term used was at first "passive GEOS"; the word GEOS had been used to designate the purpose of some of the Explorer satellites.

PEGASUS

Named after the mythical winged horse, because these satellites look as if they had very large wings. The wings are micro-meteorite detectors. Three of them were carried into orbit during the ten test shots of the first type of Saturn rocket.

| POLYOT | Name of two Russian experimental satellites that could change orbits in space. The name means "flight" and is pronounced *pol-YOT* with accent on the last syllable. |
|---|---|
| PROTON | Very heavy Russian research satellites. Name presumably was given because one of their jobs was detection of protons (cosmic rays) in space. |
| RELAY | One of the early experimental communications satellites. |
| SAMOS | American military satellite; the letters stand for Satellite and Missile Observation System. |
| SAN MARCO | Name of two Italian research satellites in orbits of very small inclination. One suspects that it was a Venetian who gave the project the name of the patron saint of Venice. |
| SCORE | An Atlas missile orbited for broadcasting tape-recorded messages. Letters stand for Signal Communications by Orbiting Relay Equipment. |
| SECOR | An Army satellite launched with an Air Force experiment. Letters mean Sequential Collation of Range; for measuring precise distances between points on the ground. |
| SOLRAD | See GREB. |
| SOYUZ | Pronounced *so-YOOZ*, with accent on last syllable, meaning "union" or "federation." "Third generation" of Russian |

manned spacecraft, for up to five cosmonauts.

SPUTNIK  First type of Russian research satellites. Name is pronounced *SPOOT-nik* with accent on first syllable. It means "road companion," as explained in the text. Proper plural is *sputniki*.

SRS  The letters stand for Solar Radiation Satellite. Small experimental satellites. See also GREB.

STARAD  An Air Force satellite launched to measure the intensity of radiation in the artificial radiation belt named Starfish, produced by the explosion of a small atomic bomb in orbit. The name, of course, is a contraction of STARfish RADiation.

SURVEYOR  Name for American unmanned moon-landing devices. The series comprised seven shots, of which five were successful.

SYNCOM  A communications satellite in the 24-hour orbit. Also the name of the first such satellite.

TELSTAR  The first commercial communications satellite, owned by Americain Telegraph & Telephone Company and orbited for the company by NASA. The name indicated: telecommunications via the stars. The Telstar satellites were superseded by the Intelsat satellites.

TIROS  American weather research satellites. The letters stand for Television and infrared Observation Satellite.

142

| | |
|---|---|
| TRAAC | Experimental Navy satellite for developing the Transit navigational satellite. Letters stand for Transit Research and Attitude Control Satellite. |
| TRANSIT | U.S. Navy satellites for aiding navigation in bad weather. |
| TRS | Small experimental satellite; the letters stand for Tetrahedral Research Satellite; its shape was the solid body called tetrahedron by mathematicians, a pyramid bound by four congruent triangles. However, the same designation is also used for octahedral satellites. |
| VELA | Originally called Vela Hotel. They are radiation detectors in very large orbits: Vela-VI has its perigee at 63,258 miles and its apogee at 75,564 miles, with an orbital period of 111 hours and 46 minutes. Everything about it is secret. |
| VENERA | Name of the Russian Venus probes; the word is the Russian name of the planet Venus. It is pronounced *ven-YAY-ra*, with the accent on the middle syllable. |
| VOSKHOD | Pronounced *vos-KHOD*, with guttural "kh" and accent on second syllable, meaning "sunrise." The "second generation" of Russian manned spacecraft, for three cosmonauts. |
| VOSTOK | Pronounced *vos-TOK*, with accent on second syllable. The first type of Russian manned spacecraft for one cosmonaut. Name means "East," but was |

given because the first Russian sailing vessel that circumnavigated the earth bore that name.

WRESAT

Australian research satellite; the letters stand for Weapons Research Establishment Satellite. It investigated radiation in the ionosphere, solar radiation, etc.

ZOND

Russian research satellites of large size, mostly used as planetary or lunar probe. The name is actually the French word *sonde*, also used in English with the meaning of "probe."

# Glossary of Rocket Names

(Only IRBMs and ICBMs and Satellite Launchers are listed—
no tactical missiles or battlefield rockets. IRBM means Inter-
mediate Range Ballistic Missile, range between 1200 and 3000
miles; ICBM means Intercontinental Ballistic Missile, with a
range longer than 4000 miles.)

AGENA            An upper stage flown with Thor, Delta, and
Atlas rockets. Fuel is unsymmetrical di-
methyl hydrazine and nitric acid. Thrust is
16,000 pounds. Amount of fuel carried is
13,500 pounds and up, depending on mission. Diameter is 5 feet; length varies with
payload and has been as much as 40 feet.
Weight of the Agena without fuel and
without payload is 1484 pounds.

ATLAS            An Air Force ICBM with a range of over
7000 miles, usually called a 1½-stage rocket
because the booster that is jettisoned is
smaller than the rocket that continues.
Three engines, total takeoff thrust 360,000
pounds in the early and 380,000 pounds in
the later versions. Takeoff weight around

**145**

270,000 pounds, depending on warhead or payload. Was used in the Mercury program and as launch vehicle for heavy satellites. Height of the missile version is 82 feet, diameter 10 feet. Fuels: kerosene and liquid oxygen.

BLUE STREAK   British IRBM that was to be about 70 feet tall and 10 feet in diameter; the fuels were kerosene and liquid oxygen. Development as a weapon was stopped when American Thor missiles became available, but the rocket was adapted to form the first stage of the *Europa-1* (*q.v.*).

CENTAUR   The first rocket designed for burning liquid hydrogen with liquid oxygen; flown as the upper stage of an Atlas for orbiting heavy satellites or launching planetary probes. Centaur is 42 feet long, with a diameter of 10 feet. Weight at separation from Atlas is 32,000 pounds; the thrust developed by two engines is 30,000 pounds.

DELTA   NASA's Delta launch vehicle is, so to speak, the result of a marriage between the Thor and the Vanguard. The first stage is a developed Thor missile; the second and third stages are developed versions of the Vanguard's second and third stages. Overall height of the rocket is 90 feet; maximum diameter, 8 feet. Takeoff weight (with 650-pound payload) is 132,300 pounds, takeoff thrust about 172,000 pounds. In 1964 three solid-fuel "strap-on" boosters were added; they are the same as the second stage of the Scout. Takeoff weight of this "thrust augmented Delta" (TAD) is 27,400 pounds higher than without the solid-fuel boosters, but the takeoff thrust is increased to 330,000 pounds. The "Improved Delta" (1965) has a larger second stage and the three "strap-ons."

DIAMANT

The French satellite launcher *Diamant* (diamond) is a three-stage rocket consisting of an *Emeraude* (emerald) rocket, with a second stage called *Topaze* and an (unnamed) third stage. The two upper stages are solid-fuel rockets; the *Emeraude* burns terebenthine (derived from turpentine) with nitric acid. Overall height of the *Diamant* is 62 feet, largest diameter 4.4 feet. Takeoff thrust was 59,700 pounds; takeoff weight was not released. A larger *Diamant* is under development. (When fired without the third stage the rocket was called *Saphir*.)

EUROPA-1

Three-stage satellite launcher built by ELDO, the European Launcher Development Organization. First stage is the formerly British missile Blue Streak, in this version 61½ feet tall and 10 feet in diameter. Fuels: kerosene and liquid oxygen. The second stage is the French *Coralie*, 18.7 feet tall and 6.6 feet in diameter; the fuels are unsymmetrical dimethyl hydrazine and nitrogen tetroxide ($N_2O_4$). The third stage is the (West) German *Astris*, not quite 11 feet tall and 6.6 feet in diameter; fuels are the same as those of the second stage. Overall height of the *Europa-1* is 103.8 feet.

JUPITER

Army IRBM with a range of about 1700 miles developed from the Redstone. The rocket stands 60 feet tall; the diameter is

**147**

105 inches. Takeoff weight, 110,000 pounds; takeoff thrust, 150,000 pounds. Fuels: kerosene and liquid oxygen. The Jupiter is a single-stage rocket. A few were equipped with upper stages for the launching of lunar probes; these converted missiles were known as Juno.

JUPITER-C  The Jupiter-C was an elongated Redstone with upper (solid-fuel) stages. It was used both for testing components for the Jupiter missile (then under development) and for launching the first Explorer satellites.

MINUTEMAN  An Air Force ICBM with a range of over 5000 miles, to be fired from silos. The missile is a solid-fuel rocket; weight, performance, and other data are classified.

POLARIS  A Navy IRBM, carried by submarines. It is a two-stage solid-fuel rocket with a takeoff weight of about 30,000 pounds. It stands about 30 feet tall; the diameter is variously reported as being from 4½ to 6 feet. The first version had a range of about 1200 miles, the second version about 1700 miles, the third version over 2500 miles. The rocket is launched from a submerged submarine by compressed air and ignites when breaking the surface. All other details are classified. An early version of the bottom stage of the Polaris was adapted to be the bottom stage of the satellite launcher Scout.

POSEIDON  A Navy solid-fuel missile with a range of 3000+ miles, slated to replace Polaris. No detail has been released.

**REDSTONE**
The first rocket developed for the United States by Wernher von Braun's team. The fuels were the same as in the V-2, alcohol and liquid oxygen. The rocket stood 69½ feet tall and had a diameter of 5 feet 11 inches. Range was over 200 miles. Because of the Jupiter-C (*q.v.*), the Redstone was also called Jupiter-A. Takeoff weight of the Redstone was 60,000 pounds; takeoff thrust was classified, but must have been between 90,000 and 100,000 pounds.

**SATURN**
The second U.S. rocket built for the sole purpose of spaceflight; the first was the Vanguard. The design is such that the various stages can be used with different boosters. The Saturn I consists of three stages called S-I, S-IV, and S-V. S-I burns kerosene with liquid oxygen; its diameter is 21½ feet, its overall height 82 feet. Its eight engines deliver a total thrust of 1½ million pounds. S-IV is about 40 feet tall and 18 feet in diameter. It has six engines burning hydrogen with oxygen and delivering a total of 90,000 pounds of thrust. The S-V has two engines of the same type as the S-IV, delivering 30,000 pounds of thrust. Overall height of a Saturn I is 162 feet. Takeoff weight is on the order of 930,000 pounds.

**SATURN-IB**
The Saturn-IB is a development of the first Saturn, with two main changes. It has a more powerful type of engine so that the takeoff thrust is 1.6 million pounds. The other change is that the structure weighs about 10 percent less than that of the original booster. The dimensions are the same. Saturn-IB made its test flight with an S-IVB

as the upper stage; this is really the upper stage of the Saturn-V rocket and is described under that entry.

**SATURN-V**

The complete rocket consists of the S-IC as the first stage, the S-II as the second stage, and the S-IVB as the third stage. S-IC burns kerosene with liquid oxygen; its five engines generate a takeoff thrust of 7.5 million pounds. Diameter is 33 feet, length is 138 feet. The S-II stage is 81½ feet long and the diameter 33 feet. Its five engines burn hydrogen with liquid oxygen, producing 1 million pounds of thrust. The S-IVB stage is 58 feet long and the diameter 21 feet 8 inches. It also burns hydrogen and oxygen, and its single engine develops a thrust of 200,000 pounds. By itself the Saturn-V stands about 280 feet tall, but payload adds to that length. As flown in its first test (Apollo 4) the total height was 364 feet, the takeoff weight 6.2 million pounds.

**SCOUT**

The smallest American satellite launch vehicle. Four-stage all-solid-fuel rocket; 72 feet tall, with a maximum diameter of about 4 feet. Takeoff weight 38,500 pounds; takeoff thrust 104,500 pounds.

**THOR**

Air Force IRBM, single stage, with a range of about 1700 miles. Fuels: kerosene and liquid oxygen. The rocket stands 65 feet tall and has a diameter of 8 feet. Takeoff weight 100,000+ pounds. Takeoff thrust 150,000 pounds, later uprated to 165,000 pounds. The Thor missile was adapted to be the bottom stage of the satellite launcher Delta (*q.v.*).

| TITAN | An Air Force ICBM. The now obsolete Titan I used kerosene and liquid oxygen for fuels and stood 98 feet tall with a maximum diameter of 10 feet. Takeoff thrust 300,000 pounds; takeoff weight 220,000 pounds. Titan II stands 103 feet tall and has a diameter of 10 feet. Fuels are unsymmetrical dimethyl hydrazine and nitrogen tetroxide. Takeoff thrust 430,000 pounds (2 engines); takeoff weight 330,000 pounds. Both Titan I and Titan II are two-stage rockets; Titan II was used in the Gemini program. Titan III is the same as Titan II, with an extra stage; it is not used by itself, but is the center for the Titan IIIC assembly, which is not a missile but a satellite launcher. The Titan IIIC consists of the Titan III and two large solid-fuel boosters which develop a million pounds of thrust each. |

V-2

The first large rocket, developed during the Second World War by the German army. Overall height was 47 feet, greatest diameter 20 feet 5 inches. Fuel was ethyl alcohol with an addition of 25 percent water and liquid oxygen. Ttakeoff weight was 28,200 pounds, takeoff thrust 60,000 pounds. Operational range was 190 miles; highest altitude reached by a V-2 (from the White Sands Proving Ground) was 128 miles. About 1500 V-2 rockets were fired operationally during the last year of the Second World War.

VANGUARD

The first American rocket specifically built to be a satellite launch vehicle. The first stage was a development of the Viking (*q.v.*) with the same fuels; the second stage

**151**

burned unsymmetrical dimethyl hydrazine with nitric acid; the third stage was a solid-fuel rocket. Overall height of the Vanguard was 70 feet, maximum diameter 45 inches. The Vanguard program consisted of the shots of Viking XIII and Viking XIV and twelve shots of the Vanguard rocket. Three satellites were placed into orbit.

VIKING

Name of a series of research rockets built for the Navy by the Martin Company. There were two versions: Viking I through Viking VII, 47½ feet tall with a diameter of 32 inches; Viking VIII through Viking XIV, 41½ feet tall, with a diameter of 45 inches. All shots in the Viking Program were vertical, or nearly so. Greatest altitude of the first version was reached by Viking VII on August 7, 1951; it was 136 miles. Greatest altitude of the second version was reached on May 24, 1954, by Viking XI; it was 158 miles. The Viking Program consisted of 12 shots (numero IV was fired from shipboard); Viking XIII and Viking XIV were fired in the Vanguard Program. The fuel was alcohol, burned with liquid oxygen.

X-17

American solid-fuel research rocket by Lockheed, used for testing re-entry nose cones. First stage was a Sergeant rocket with a thrust of 50,000 pounds; the second stage was a cluster of three Recruit rockets with a total thrust of 105,000 pounds; the third stage was a modified Recruit with a thrust of 36,000 pounds. The first stage lifted the others to an altitude of about 350 miles; the second and third stage then fired upside down to give a high re-entry velocity to the nose cone. In February 1957 all three stages of an X-17 fired on the way up; peak of the flight must have been 990 miles. (Not to be confused with the X-15, which was a rocket-propelled manned research airplane.)

## NOTE ON THE DESIGNATIONS OF
## THE APOLLO FLIGHTS

The first flight of a Saturn V rocket had the official designation "Apollo 4." There were no "Apollos 1, 2, 3"; at least, they were not called that at the time. The first three flights of the Saturn IB rocket tested the Apollo spacecraft but were called Saturn 11, 12, and 13. Saturn 11 (the first Saturn IB flight) on February 26, 1966, carried an Apollo spacecraft with the LM. The spacecraft then made re-entry and was recovered. Saturn 12 was also called AS-203 (AS for Apollo-Saturn) and carried a partly filled hydrogen tank to see how liquid hydrogen would behave when weightless. The date was July 5, 1966. On August 25, 1966, followed Saturn 13, also called AS-202; it was a sub-orbital flight for an Apollo spacecraft with re-entry 18,000 miles from Florida in the Pacific Ocean.

The flights designated "Apollo 5" and "Apollo 6" were two more unmanned tests, one using a Saturn IB rocket and the other a Saturn V. For "Apollo 7," "Apollo 8," and "Apollo 9," see pages 128–132.

# Tables

## TABLE 1
## THE VANGUARD SATELLITES

| No. | Launch Date | First Perigee (miles) | First Apogee (miles) | Orbital Period (min.) | Inclination | Weight (lbs.) |
|-----|-------------|-----------------------|----------------------|-----------------------|-------------|---------------|
| I | Mar. 17, 1958 | 409 | 2453 | 134.3 | 34.3° | 3.25 |
| II | Feb. 17, 1959 | 347 | 2064 | 125.9 | 32.9° | 21.5 |
| III | Sept. 18, 1959 | 319 | 2329 | 130.2 | 33.3° | 99.2 |

NOTE

All three Vanguard satellites are in permanent orbits.

157

## TABLE 2

## THE EXPLORER SATELLITES

| No. | Launch Date | First Perigee (mi.) | First Apogee (mi.) | Orbital Period | Weight (lbs.) | Inclination | Status as of Jan. 1, 1969 (or re-entry date) |
|---|---|---|---|---|---|---|---|
| I | Jan. 31, 1958 | 224 | 1,573 | 114.7 min. | 31 | 33.3° | orbiting |
| III | Mar. 26, 1958 | 121 | 1,746 | 115.9 min. | 31 | 33.5° | June 27, 1958 |
| IV | July 26, 1958 | 163 | 1,380 | 110.3 min. | 37.4 | 50.3° | Oct. 23, 1959 |
| VI | Aug. 7, 1959 | 157 | 26,400 | 12 hrs. 48 min. | 143.3 | 47.0° | July 1961 |
| VII | Oct. 13, 1959 | 346 | 664 | 101.2 min. | 92.8 | 50.3° | orbiting |
| VIII | Nov. 3, 1960 | 258 | 1,423 | 112.7 min. | 90.3 | 50.0° | orbiting |
| IX | Feb. 16, 1961 | 395 | 1,605 | 118.3 min. | 15.4 | 38.6° | Apr. 9, 1964 |
| X | Mar. 25, 1961 | 110 | 112,500 | 112 hrs. | 79.4 | 33.0° | unknown |
| XI | Apr. 27, 1961 | 302 | 1,113 | 108.1 min. | 81.5 | 28.8° | orbiting |
| XII | Aug. 15, 1961 | 182 | 48,032 | 26 hrs. 25 min. | 81.5 | 33.3° | orbiting |
| XIII | Aug. 25, 1961 | 275 | 565 | 97.3 min. | 187.4 | 36.5° | orbiting |
| XIV | Oct. 2, 1962 | 175 | 61,000 | 36 hrs. 24 min. | 88.2 | 32.9° | unknown |
| XV | Oct. 27, 1962 | 191 | 10,912 | 5 hrs. 12 min. | 99.2 | 18.0° | unknown |
| XVI | Dec. 16, 1962 | 472 | 727 | 104.4 min. | 220.5 | 52.0° | orbiting |
| XVII | Apr. 2, 1963 | 163 | 546 | 96.4 min. | 405.6 | 57.6° | Nov. 24, 1966 |
| XVIII | Nov. 26, 1963 | 119 | 122,793 | 96 hrs. 20 min. | 138.9 | 33.3° | unknown |

| | | | | | | | |
|---|---|---|---|---|---|---|---|
| XIX | Dec. 19, 1963 | 367 | 1,488 | 115.9 min. | 17.6 | 78.6° | orbiting |
| XX | Aug. 25, 1964 | 540 | 615 | 103.9 min. | 97.0 | 79.9° | orbiting |
| XXI | Oct. 3, 1964 | 120 | 59,400 | 35 hours | 136.7 | 33.5° | Jan. 1966 |
| XXII | Oct. 9, 1964 | 549 | 669 | 104.7 min. | 116.8 | 79.7° | orbiting |
| XXIII | Nov. 6, 1964 | 286 | 614 | 99.2 min. | 295.4 | 51.9° | orbiting |
| XXIV | Nov. 21, 1964 | 327 | 1,552 | 116.3 min. | 19.8 | 81.4° | orbiting |
| XXV | same | same | same | same | 90.4 | same | orbiting |
| XXVI | Dec. 21, 1964 | 193 | 16,290 | 7 hrs. 36 min. | 101.4 | 20.2° | unknown |
| XXVII | Apr. 29, 1965 | 592 | 816 | 107.8 min. | 132.3 | 41.2° | orbiting |
| XXVIII | May 29, 1965 | 122 | 164,167 | 142 hrs. 40 min. | 130.0 | 33.9° | July 4, 1968 |
| XXIX | Nov. 6, 1965 | 697 | 1,410 | 120 min. | 385.8 | 59.4° | orbiting |
| XXX | Nov. 18, 1965 | 425 | 564 | 102.8 min. | 125.6 | 59.4° | orbiting |
| XXXI | Nov. 28, 1965 | 315 | 1,853 | 121.3 min. | 218.2 | 79.8° | orbiting |
| XXXII | May 25, 1966 | 175 | 1,695 | 116.0 min. | 496.0 | 64.7° | orbiting |
| XXXIII | July 1, 1966 | 9,881 | 270,562 | 142 hrs. 20 min. | 211.6 | 28.7° | orbiting |
| XXXIV | May 24, 1967 | 150 | 133,211 | 106 hours | 163.6 | 67.0° | May 2, 1969 |

NOTES

Nos. II and V failed to reach orbit.

Nos. XXIV and XXV were orbited by the same rocket.

Nos. IX, XXI, and XXIV were balloon satellites.

No. XXXI also carried Canada's Alouette II into orbit.

No. XXXIII was supposed to orbit the moon, but was too fast when it reached the moon's vicinity and went about 20,000 miles farther out into space, finally settling in the orbit given in the table.

159

## TABLE 3

### THE ORBIT OF EXPLORER-I FROM JULY 1965 TO THE END OF 1968 AS AN EXAMPLE OF SLOW ORBITAL DECAY

(During February 1,1958, the first day in orbit, the perigee was at 224 miles, the apogee at 1573 miles; the orbital period was 114.8 minutes. Throughout, the inclination remained close to 33°.)

| Date | Perigee (miles) | Apogee (miles) | Orbital Period (minutes) |
|---|---|---|---|
| July 15, 1965 | 213 | 968 | 104.1 |
| Dec. 15, 1965 | 211 | 954 | 103.9 |
| July 15, 1966 | 211 | 936 | 103.5 |
| Dec. 15, 1966 | 210 | 906 | 103.0 |
| July 15, 1967 | 209 | 841 | 101.9 |
| Dec. 15, 1967 | 207.5 | 785 | 100.8 |
| July 15, 1968 | 202 | 703 | 99.4 |
| Dec. 15, 1968 | 202 | 638 | 98.3 |
| Dec. 31, 1968 | 200 | 632 | 98.1 |

160

TABLE 4

## THE DISCOVERER SATELLITES

| No. | Launch Date | First Perigee (mi.) | First Apogee (mi.) | Orbital Period (min.) | Lifetime Terminated |
|---|---|---|---|---|---|
| I | Feb. 28, 1959 | 99 | 602 | 95.9 | Mar. 5, 1959 |
| II | Apr. 13, 1959 | 142 | 220 | 90.5 | Apr. 26, 1959 |
| V | Aug. 13, 1959 | 150 | 450 | 95 | Sept. 28, 1959 |
| VI | Aug. 19, 1959 | 138 | 537 | 100 | Oct. 20, 1959 |
| VII | Nov. 7, 1959 | 100 | 515 | 94.5 | Nov. 26, 1959 |
| VIII | Nov. 20, 1959 | 117 | 1040 | 103 | Mar. 1961 |
| XI | Apr. 15, 1960 | 110 | 345 | 92.3 | Apr. 26, 1960 |
| XIII | Aug. 10, 1960 | 1018 | 1160 | 121.5 | Aug. 11, 1960 |
| XIV | Aug. 18, 1960 | 266 | 438 | 96 | Aug. 19, 1960 |
| XV | Sept. 13, 1960 | 130 | 472 | 94.2 | Sept. 14, 1960 |
| XVII | Nov. 12, 1960 | 118 | 615 | 96 | Dec. 29, 1960 |
| XVIII | Dec. 7, 1960 | 154 | 459 | 93.8 | Apr. 2, 1961 |
| XIX | Dec. 20, 1960 | 128 | 391 | 93 | Jan. 23, 1961 |
| XX | Feb. 17, 1961 | 177 | 486 | 95.4 | July 28, 1962 |
| XXI | Feb. 18, 1961 | 149 | 659 | 93.8 | Apr. 20, 1962 |
| XXIII | Apr. 8, 1961 | — | — | — | Apr. 16, 1962 |
| XXV | June 16, 1961 | 139 | 252 | 91 | July 12, 1961 |
| XXVI | July 7, 1961 | 142 | 410 | 93.5 | Feb. 13, 1965 |
| XXIX | Aug. 30, 1961 | 140 | 345 | 91 | Sept. 10, 1961 |
| XXX | Sept. 12, 1961 | 154 | 345 | 92 | Dec. 12, 1961 |
| XXXI | Sept. 17, 1961 | 152 | 255 | 91 | Oct. 26, 1961 |
| XXXII | Oct. 13, 1961 | 141 | 246 | 91 | Nov. 13, 1961 |
| XXXIV | Nov. 5, 1961 | 134 | 637 | 105 | Dec. 7, 1961 |
| XXXV | Nov. 15, 1961 | 147 | 137 | 90.5 | Dec. 3, 1961 |
| XXXVI | Dec. 12, 1961 | 148 | 280 | 91 | Mar. 8, 1962 |
| XXXVIII | Feb. 27. 1962 | — | — | — | Mar. 21, 1962 |
| ??? | July 28, 1962 | 116.8 | 215.6 | 89.9 | Aug. 24, 1962 |

### NOTES

Since the Discoverer Program was a military program, carried out by the Air Force, a certain amount of secrecy was involved. Missing numbers would normally indicate that the satellite failed to reach orbit, but in this case it also means that it was only revealed that "a classified satellite had been launched" and that a secret satellite might have had a Discoverer number. The last satellite in the list did not have a Discoverer number, but its orbit indicates that it belongs to this series of satellite shots. Along with Discoverer XXXVI, the amateur radio satellite OSCAR-I was orbited; it re-entered on January 31, 1962.

# TABLE 5

## AMERICAN CLOUD COVER (WEATHER WATCH) SATELLITES

| Name | Launch Date | First Perigee (mi.) | First Apogee (mi.) | Inclination | Orbital Period (min.) | Weight (lbs.) |
|---|---|---|---|---|---|---|
| TIROS I | Apr. 1, 1960 | 429 | 468 | 48.3° | 99.1 | 270 |
| II | Nov. 23, 1960 | 406 | 431 | 48.5° | 98.0 | 280 |
| III | July 12, 1961 | 457 | 510 | 47.8° | 100.3 | 285 |
| IV | Feb. 8, 1962 | 471 | 525 | 48.2° | 99.2 | 285 |
| V | June 19, 1962 | 367 | 604 | 58.1° | 100.5 | 285 |
| VI | Sept. 18 1962 | 425 | 442 | 58.3° | 98.7 | 281 |
| VII | June 19, 1963 | 385 | 405 | 58.2° | 97.4 | 297 |
| VIII | Dec. 21, 1963 | 429 | 476 | 58.4° | 99.3 | 262 |
| Nimbus I | Aug. 28, 1964 | 260 | 580 | 98.7° | 96.8 | 830 |
| TIROS IX | Jan. 22, 1965 | 435 | 1602 | 96.3° | 119.2 | 305 |
| X | July 2, 1965 | 376 | 522 | 98.5° | 100.7 | 300 |
| ESSA I | Feb. 3, 1966 | 433 | 523 | 97.8° | 100.3 | 305 |
| II | Feb. 28, 1966 | 844 | 881 | 100.8° | 113.5 | 290 |
| Nimbus II | May 15, 1966 | 685 | 733 | 100.3° | 108.0 | 912 |
| ESSA III | Oct. 2, 1966 | 863 | 925 | 101.0° | 114.6 | 300 |
| IV | Jan. 26, 1967 | 826 | 896 | 101.9° | 113.4 | 300 |
| V | Apr. 20, 1967 | 844 | 885 | 101.9° | 113.5 | 300 |
| VI | Nov. 10, 1967 | 876 | 925 | 102.0° | 114.8 | 300 |
| VII | Aug. 16, 1968 | 890 | 916 | 101.7° | 114.9 | 320 |
| VIII | Dec. 15, 1968 | 881 | 910 | 101.8° | 114.6 | 320 |
| IX | Feb. 26, 1969 | 887 | 936 | 101.7° | 115.2 | 320 |
| Nimbus III | Apr. 14, 1969 | 671 | 707 | 99.9° | 107.4 | 800 |

NOTE
All these satellites are in permanent orbits.

## TABLE 6

## AMERICAN COMMUNICATION SATELLITES

| Name | Launch Date | First Perigee (miles) | First Apogee (miles) | Inclination | Orbital Period | Weight (lbs.) |
|------|-------------|----------------------|---------------------|-------------|----------------|---------------|
| Echo I | Aug. 12, 1960 | 1,018 | 1,160 | 47.3° | 121.6 min. | 137.4 |
| Telstar I | July 10, 1962 | 593 | 3,503 | 44.7° | 157.5 min. | 170 |
| Relay I | Dec. 13, 1962 | 829 | 4,611 | 47.5° | 185 min. | 172 |
| Syncom I | Feb. 14, 1963 | 21,269 | 23,000 | 31.0° | 23 hrs. 56 min. | 86 |
| Telstar II | May 7, 1963 | 603 | 6,712 | 42.7° | 225.2 min. | 175 |
| Syncom II | July 26, 1963 | 22,184 | 22,221 | 29.5° | 23 hrs. 55.9 min. | 79 |
| Relay II | Jan. 21, 1964 | 1,290 | 4,612 | 46.3° | 194.7 min. | 172 |
| Echo II | Jan. 25, 1964 | 621 | 831 | 81.4° | 108.7 min. | 147 |
| Early Bird | Apr. 6, 1965 | 21,715 | 21,726 | 3.3° | 23 hrs. 57.3 min. | 84 |
| INTELSAT II-F 1 | Oct. 26, 1966 | 2,126 | 23,322 | 18.0° | 12 hrs. 10 min. | |
| ATS-I | Dec. 7, 1966 | 22,277 | 22,920 | 1.0° | 24 hrs. 26 min. | 775 |
| INTELSAT II-F 2 | Jan. 11, 1967 | 22,226 | 22,250 | 0.7° | 23 hrs. 56.2 min. | |
| INTELSAT II-F 3 | Mar. 23, 1967 | 22,245 | 23,741 | 0.1° | 23 hrs. 56.1 min. | |
| ATS-II | Apr. 6, 1967 | 118 | 6,447 | 28.3° | 212.5 min. | 560 |
| INTELSAT II-F 4 | Sept. 28, 1967 | 190 | 22,915 | 0.0° | 10 hrs. 54.8 min. | |
| ATS-III | Nov. 5, 1967 | 22,228 | 22,253 | 0.7° | 23 hrs. 56.4 min. | 560 |
| INTELSAT III-F 2 | Dec. 19, 1968 | 22,239 | 22,251 | 0.7° | 23 hrs. 5.9 min. | |
| INTELSAT III-F 3 | Feb. 6, 1969 | 22,236 | 22,250 | 1.3° | 23 hrs. 55.4 min. | |

The United States also maintains a network of at least 18 military communications satellites of which little is known, except that they were orbited by Titan IIIC rockets and are spaced around the earth at a distance of about 21,000 miles, with orbital periods near 21 hours, 15 minutes.

The current orbit of Syncom I is not known.

Echo I re-entered and burned up on May 24, 1968.

## TABLE 7

### THE PROTON SATELLITES

| No. | Launch Date | First Perigee (miles) | First Apogee (miles) | Weight (lbs.) | Orbital Period (minutes) | Lifetime Terminated |
|-----|-------------|----------------------|---------------------|---------------|------------------------|--------------------|
| I | July 16, 1965 | 108.7 | 279.5 | 26,896 | 90.9 | Oct. 11, 1965 |
| II | Nov. 2, 1965 | 118.5 | 396.0 | 26,840 | 92.6 | Feb. 6, 1966 |
| III | July 6, 1966 | 114.6 | 361.0 | 26,200 | 92.3 | Sept. 16, 1966 |
| IV | Nov. 16, 1968 | 154.7 | 283.3 | 37,478 | 91.5 | orbiting |

## TABLE 8

### THE ELEKTRON SATELLITES

| No. | Launch Date | First Perigee (miles) | First Apogee (miles) | Orbital Period (minutes) |
|-----|-------------|----------------------|---------------------|-------------------------|
| I | Jan. 31, 1964 | 250 | 4,423.5 | 169.3 |
| II | same | 363 | 42,152.5 | 1356.3 |
| III | July 11, 1964 | 251 | 4,350 | 168 |
| IV | same | 283 | 40,886 | 1314 |

### NOTE
Both pairs are still orbiting; each pair was orbited by the same rocket.

## TABLE 9

### THE MOLNIYA SATELLITES

| No. | Launch Date | First Perigee (miles) | First Apogee (miles) | Inclination | Orbital Period |
|---|---|---|---|---|---|
| 1 | Apr. 23, 1965 | 375.5 | 24,780 | 65.5° | 12 hrs. 0.3 min. |
| 2 | Oct. 13, 1965 | 348 | 24,695 | 64.9° | 11 hrs. 59 min. |
| 3 | Apr. 25, 1966 | 310 | 24,509 | 65.0° | 11 hrs. 50.5 min. |
| 4 | Oct. 20, 1966 | 309 | 24,863 | 64.9° | 12 hrs. 9 min. |
| 5 | May 24, 1967 | 287 | 24,719 | 64.8° | 11 hrs. 50.4 min. |
| 6 | Oct. 3, 1967 | 53 | 4,680 | 65.2° | 2 hrs. 50.5 min. |
| 7 | Oct. 22, 1967 | 289 | 25,267 | 64.7° | 12 hrs. 13.5 min. |
| 8 | Apr. 21, 1968 | 454 | 24,613 | 65.1° | 11 hrs. 57.5 min. |
| 9 | July 6, 1968 | 353 | 24,711 | 65.0° | 11 hrs. 57.3 min. |
| 10 | Oct. 5, 1968 | 252 | 24,824 | 65.1° | 11 hrs. 57.8 min. |
| 11 | Apr. 11, 1969 | 300 | 24,553 | 64.9° | 11 hrs. 52.1 min. |

### NOTES

No. 2 re-entered March 17, 1967.
No. 3 re-entered September 11, 1968.
No. 6 re-entered March 4, 1969; others are orbiting.

## TABLE 10

### THE SPUTNIK SATELLITES

| No. | Launch Date | First Perigee (miles) | First Apogee (miles) | Orbital Period (min.) | Weight (lbs.) | Lifetime Terminated |
|---|---|---|---|---|---|---|
| 1 | Oct. 4, 1957 | 142 | 588 | 96.2 | 183 | Jan. 4, 1958 |
| 2 | Nov. 3, 1957 | 140 | 1038 | 103.7 | 1,120 | Apr. 19, 1958 |
| 3 | May 15, 1958 | 135 | 1167 | 106.0 | 2,925 | Apr. 6, 1960 |
| 4 | May 15, 1960 | 189 | 222 | 91.1 | 9,988 | July 17, 1960 |
| 5 | Aug. 19, 1960 | 199 | 159 | 90.7 | 10,120 | Aug. 20, 1960 |
| 6 | Dec. 1, 1960 | 116 | 165 | 88.6 | 10,060 | Dec. 3, 1960 |
| 7 | Feb. 4, 1961 | 139 | 204 | 90.0 | 14,290 | Feb. 26, 1961 |
| 8 | Feb. 12, 1961 | 123 | 202 | 90.0 | 14,300 | Feb. 25, 1961 |
| 9 | Mar. 9, 1961 | 110 | 155 | 88.2 | 10,360 | Mar. 9, 1961 |
| 10 | Mar. 25, 1961 | 110 | 153 | 88.0 | 10,360 | Mar. 25, 1961 |

### NOTE

No. 4 temporarily assumed an orbit with a perigee at 189 miles, an apogee at 412 miles, and an orbital period of 94.3 minutes.

TABLE 11

RUSSIAN KOSMOS SATELLITES IN PERMANENT ORBITS

| No. | Launch Date | Perigee (mi.) | Apogee (mi.) | Orbital Period (min.) | Inclination (degrees) | |
|---|---|---|---|---|---|---|
| 41 | Aug. 22, 1964 | 1188 | 24,794 | 714.7 | 68.6 | |
| 44 | Aug. 28, 1964 | 384 | 534 | 99.4 | 65.0 | |
| 58 | Feb. 21, 1965 | 361 | 409 | 96.9 | 65.0 | |
| 71 | July 16, 1965 | 288 | 302 | 94.1 | 56.0 | |
| 72 | same | 327 | 345 | 95.4 | same | orbited by one rocket |
| 73 | same | 319 | 321 | 94.9 | same | |
| 74 | same | 329 | 364 | 95.8 | same | |
| 75 | same | 329 | 378 | 96.0 | same | |
| 80 | Sept. 3, 1965 | 846 | 961 | 114.9 | 56.0 | |
| 81 | same | 864 | 963 | 115.3 | same | orbited by one rocket |
| 82 | same | 880 | 966 | 115.6 | same | |
| 83 | same | 896 | 972 | 116.0 | same | |
| 84 | same | 913 | 976 | 116.4 | same | |
| 86 | Sept. 18, 1965 | 795 | 1016 | 115.0 | 56.0 | |
| 87 | same | 813 | 1021 | 115.4 | same | orbited by one rocket |
| 88 | same | 825 | 1031 | 115.8 | same | |
| 89 | same | 841 | 1038 | 116.2 | same | |
| 90 | same | 856 | 1046 | 116.6 | same | |
| 100 | Dec. 17, 1965 | 393 | 407 | 97.4 | 64.9 | |
| 103 | Dec. 28, 1965 | 368 | 395 | 96.8 | 56.0 | |
| 118 | May 11, 1966 | 365 | 423 | 96.9 | 65.0 | |
| 122 | June 25, 1966 | 342 | 427 | 96.9 | 64.9 | |
| 144 | Feb. 28, 1967 | 361 | 395 | 96.6 | 81.2 | |
| 151 | Mar. 24, 1967 | 368 | 404 | 97.0 | 56.0 | |
| 156 | Apr. 27, 1967 | 335 | 441 | 96.7 | 81.1 | |
| 158 | May 15, 1967 | 458 | 511 | 100.4 | 74.0 | |
| 159 | May 17, 1967 | 1376 | 36,506 | 1173.7 | 52.7 | |

| No. | Launch Date | Perigee (mi.) | Apogee (mi.) | Orbital Period (min.) | Inclination (degrees) |
|---|---|---|---|---|---|
| 174 | Aug. 31, 1967 | 310 | 24,700 | 493.1 | 65.0 |
| 184 | Oct. 24, 1967 | 374 | 396 | 96.9 | 81.1 |
| 185 | Oct. 27, 1967 | 322 | 542 | 93.3 | 64.0 |
| 189 | Oct. 30, 1967 | 325 | 361 | 95.3 | 74.0 |
| 192 | Nov. 23, 1967 | 462 | 469 | 99.7 | 74.0 |
| 198 | Dec. 27, 1967 | 556 | 590 | 103.4 | 65.1 |
| 200 | Jan. 19, 1968 | 322 | 334 | 94.8 | 74.0 |
| 203 | Feb. 20, 1968 | 737 | 747 | 109.2 | 74.0 |
| 204 | Mar. 5, 1968 | 317 | 549 | 98.5 | 59.4 |
| 206 | Mar. 14, 1968 | 372 | 408 | 96.9 | 81.2 |
| 209 | Mar. 22, 1968 | 142 | 165 | 103.1 | 65.3 |
| 219 | Apr. 26, 1968 | 140 | 1085 | 95.8 | 48.3 |
| 220 | May 7, 1968 | 420 | 469 | 99.0 | 74.0 |
| 221 | May 24, 1968 | 133 | 1293 | 102.8 | 48.3 |
| 236 | Aug. 27, 1968 | 368 | 387 | 96.8 | 56.0 |
| 248 | Oct. 19, 1968 | 290 | 340 | 94.7 | 62.2 |
| 249 | Oct. 20, 1968 | 306 | 1340 | 112.1 | 62.3 |
| 250 | Oct. 30, 1968 | 322 | 335 | 95.2 | 74.0 |
| 252 | Nov. 1, 1968 | 329 | 1335 | 112.4 | 62.3 |
| 256 | Nov. 30, 1968 | 729 | 762 | 109.4 | 74.0 |
| 260 | Dec. 16, 1968 | 324 | 24,581 | 712.3 | 64.9 |
| 262 | Dec. 26, 1968 | 160 | 465 | 95.2 | 48.4 |

## TABLE 12
## THE INTERNATIONAL SATELLITES

| Name | Country | Launch Date | First Perigee (mi.) | First Apogee (mi.) | Orbital Period (min.) | Weight (lbs.) | Lifetime Terminated |
|---|---|---|---|---|---|---|---|
| Ariel I | U.K. | Apr. 26, 1962 | 242 | 754 | 95 | 132 | orbiting |
| Alouette | Canada | Sept. 27, 1962 | 597 | 619 | 105.4 | 319 | orbiting |
| Ariel II | U.K. | Mar. 27, 1964 | 186 | 825 | 101.2 | 150 | orbiting |
| San Marco I | Italy | Dec. 15, 1964 | 125 | 490 | 94.7 | 254 | Sept. 13, 1965 |
| A-1 | France | Nov. 26, 1965 | 327 | 1114 | 108.5 | 135 | orbiting |
| Alouette II | Canada | Nov. 28, 1965 | 469 | 478 | 99.9 | 132 | orbiting |
| FR-1 | France | Dec. 6, 1965 | 462 | 471 | 99.8 | | orbiting |
| D-1A | France | Feb. 17, 1966 | 312 | 1710 | 118.1 | 41.8 | orbiting |
| Diadème 1 | France | Feb. 8, 1967 | 311 | 1701 | 104.2 | 200 | orbiting |
| Diadème 2 | France | Feb. 15, 1967 | 367 | 1168 | 110.2 | 200 | orbiting |
| San Marco II | Italy | Apr. 26, 1967 | 135 | 498 | 94.7 | 280 | Oct. 14, 1967 |
| Ariel III | U.K. | May 5, 1967 | 306 | 373 | 95.6 | 175 | orbiting |
| Wresat | Australia | Nov. 29, 1967 | 106 | 776 | 98.9 | 160 | Jan. 10, 1968 |
| IRIS (ESRO-II) | ESRO | May 17, 1968 | 205 | 677 | 98.9 | 163 | orbiting |
| Aurora (ESRO-I) | ESRO | Oct. 3, 1968 | 160 | 871 | 101.4 | 185 | orbiting |
| HEOS-A | ESRO | Dec. 5, 1968 | 273 | 139,458 | 105 hrs. 51.8 min. | | orbiting |
| ISIS-A | Canada | Jan. 30, 1969 | 373 | 2184 | 128.4 | 532 | orbiting |

NOTES

All three Ariels, both Alouettes, the three ESRO satellites, ISIS-A, and FR-1 were orbited by American-built rockets from U.S. territory by international crews. San Marco I was orbited by an American rocket from U.S. territory by an Italian firing crew. San Marco II was orbited by an American rocket by an Italian crew from a floating platform off the East African coast. Wresat used an American rocket from Australian territory, while A-1, Diadème I, and Diadème 2 were orbited with the French *Diamant* rocket.

# TABLE 13

## SATELLITES AND SPACE JUNK
## 1957–1968

| Year of Launch | Satellites by Country | | | | Still Orbiting (January 31, 1969) | |
|---|---|---|---|---|---|---|
| | USA | USSR | Others | Space Junk | Satellites | Space Junk |
| 1957 | — | 2 | — | 4 | — | — |
| 1958 | 5 | 1 | — | 9 | 2 | 2 |
| 1959 | 10 | — | — | 15 | 3 | 2 |
| 1960 | 16 | 3 | — | 24 | 7 | 17 |
| 1961 | 33 | 6 | — | 52 | 9 | 13 [1] |
| 1962 | 43 | 14 | 2 | 69 | 11 | 29 |
| 1963 | 37 | 15 | — | 70 | 9 | 63 [2] |
| 1964 | 56 | 32 | 2 | 115 | 28 | 54 |
| 1965 | 66 | 53 | 3 | 145 | 60 | 95 [3] |
| 1966 | 80 | 34 | 2 | 137 | 37 | 91 |
| 1967 | 63 | 65 | 4 | 152 | 50 | 86 |
| 1968 | 41 | 72 | 3 | 213 | 48 | 71 [4] |
| | 450 | 297 | 16 | 1005 | 264 | 523 |

## NOTES

Manned flights in earth orbit are counted as satellites; satellites owned by industry are counted under USA, since the companies involved are American or, in one case, partly American-owned.

A number of shots produced large numbers of small orbiting objects because of explosions that have never been officially explained. There were:

[1] 215 objects associated with the American satellites Transit-4A and Injun-SR-3, launched June 29, 1961.

[2] 79 objects associated with American (military) satellite 1963-14A, launched May 9, 1963.

[3] 131 objects associated with Soviet satellite 1965-20A, launched March 15, 1965; 382 objects associated with 1965-82A, the fourth shot of a Titan IIIC rocket on October 15, 1965; 14 objects were associated with Soviet satellite Kosmos-103, launched December 28, 1965.

[4] 42 objects associated with Soviet satellite Kosmos-249, launched October 20, 1968; 42 objects associated with Soviet satellite Kosmos-252, launched November 1, 1968; 22 objects associated with Soviet satellite Kosmos-261, launched December 19, 1968.

Most of these minor objects have re-entered in the meantime.

Number of lunar probes (both USA and USSR) that struck the moon or soft-landed on the moon: 23.

Number of planetary probes (both USA and USSR) now in orbits around the sun: 22.

## TABLE 14

### THE RANGER PROGRAM (LUNAR PROBES)

| No. | Launch Date | Results |
|---|---|---|
| VI | Jan. 30, 1964 | Good flight path, but cameras failed to work |
| VII | July 28, 1964 | transmitted 4316 photographs |
| VIII | Feb. 17, 1965 | transmitted 7137 photographs |
| IX | Mar. 21, 1965 | transmitted 5814 photographs |

#### NOTE

The Ranger Program began with attempts just to shoot to the moon. Ranger VI was the first that was supposed to strike the moon but transmit pictures before impact. It had a camera failure, and all the Rangers before No. VI were also failures of one kind or another. The last three produced excellent results.

170

## TABLE 15

### THE LUNAR ORBITERS

| No. | Launch Date | Remarks |
|-----|-------------|---------|
| I | Aug. 10, 1966 | equatorial orbit |
| II | Nov. 7, 1966 | same |
| III | Feb. 4, 1967 | same |
| IV | May 4, 1967 | polar orbit |
| V | Aug. 2, 1967 | same |

### NOTE

The terms "equatorial" and "polar" refer to the moon's equator and poles. The first Lunar Orbiter suffered a failure of one set of its two sets of cameras; all others performed perfectly. Pictures were taken when the spacecraft was about 31 miles above the lunar surface. The pictures were not TV pictures, but were on film, which was automatically developed and then transmitted. When the film was used up, the spacecraft crashed on the moon.

## TABLE 16
### THE SURVEYOR PROGRAM (LUNAR)

| No. | Launch Date | Results |
|---|---|---|
| I | May 30, 1966 | Landing accomplished; transmitted over 10,400 pictures |
| II | Sept. 20, 1966 | Tumbled in flight; crashed on moon Sept. 23, 1966 |
| III | Apr. 17, 1967 | Landing accomplished; had mechanical scoop for digging small trenches |
| IV | July 14, 1967 | Retro-rocket exploded; failure |
| V | Sept. 8, 1967 | Landing accomplished; also had mechanical scoop |
| VI | Nov. 7, 1967 | Landing accomplished; took off from moon for small jump |
| VII | Jan. 6, 1968 | Landing accomplished; had mechanical scoop. |

### NOTE

The digging scoop had the purpose of finding out how hard the lunar soil is; it was found to be equal to hard soil on earth. Nos. V and VII also carried a device for a rough determination of the elements present in the lunar soil. The jump of No. VI was made to photograph the imprint of the footpads made in the original landing.

## TABLE 17

### THE MARINER PROGRAM (PLANETARY)

| No. | Launch Date | Results |
|-----|-------------|---------|
| II | Aug. 27, 1962 | Fly-by near Venus on Dec. 14, 1962; shortest distance, 21,648 miles. Made temperature and other measurements. |
| III | Nov. 5, 1964 | Put into orbit to Mars, but spacecraft failed to unfold itself and therefore could not work. Failure. |
| IV | Nov. 28, 1964 | Fly-by near Mars July 14, 1965; shortest distance, slightly over 6000 miles. Made temperature and other measurements and took 22 pictures, of which a dozen were usable. |
| V | June 14, 1967 | Fly-by near Venus on Oct. 19, 1967; somewhat closer than Mariner II. Confirmed earlier measurements. |
| VI | Feb. 24, 1969 | Fly-by near Mars expected on July 31, 1969. |
| VII | Mar. 27, 1969 | Fly-by near Mars expected on Aug. 5, 1969. |

### NOTE

Mariner I was a failure. In addition to their *Zond* probes the Russians sent several other probes both to Mars and to Venus. Only *Venera 4* was successful, putting an instrument capsule into the planet's atmosphere on Oct. 17, 1967. Instrument readings were in general agreement with the findings of Mariners II and V.

173

## TABLE 18

## THE SOVIET "LUNA" PROGRAM

| No. | Launch Date | Results |
|---|---|---|
| 4 | Apr. 2, 1963 | Missed moon and went into orbit around the sun. |
| 5 | May 9, 1965 | Crashed on moon May 12, 1965. |
| 6 | June 8, 1965 | Malfunction; missed moon by 100,000 miles; now in orbit around the sun. |
| 7 | Oct. 4, 1965 | Crashed on moon Oct. 7, 1965. |
| 8 | Dec. 3, 1965 | Crashed on moon Dec. 6, 1965. |
| 9 | Jan. 31, 1966 | Landed Feb. 3, transmitted about 30 good pictures. |
| 10 | Mar. 31, 1966 | Went into orbit around moon Apr. 2, 1966. |
| 11 | Aug. 24, 1966 | Went into orbit around moon Aug. 27, 1966. |
| 12 | Oct. 25, 1966 | Went into orbit around moon Oct. 28, 1966; dead transmitter. |
| 13 | Dec. 21, 1966 | Landed Dec. 14, 1966, transmitted pictures. |
| 14 | Apr. 7, 1968 | Went into orbit around moon Apr. 10, 1968. |

### NOTE

Three space shots were originally named "Cosmic Rocket" 1, 2, and 3, but are now counted as the first three of the Luna series. The first, launched Jan. 2, 1959, passed the moon and is in orbit around the sun; the second, launched Sept. 12, 1959, struck the moon 35 hours after take-off, while the third seems to have been aimed for Venus but was unsuccessful.

## TABLE 19

### THE SOVIET "ZOND" PROGRAM

| No. | Launch Date | Results |
|---|---|---|
| 1. | Apr. 2, 1964 | Believed to have been a Venus probe; unsuccessful. |
| 2 | Nov. 30, 1964 | Mars probe; lost electrical power while underway. |
| 3 | July 18, 1965 | Passed moon; transmitted good pictures taken from a distance. |
| 4 | Mar. 2, 1968 | Failed to leave parking orbit; eventually re-entered. |
| 5 | Sept. 14, 1968 | Looped around moon with live animals aboard; landed on Sept. 21 in Indian Ocean. |
| 6 | Nov. 10, 1968 | Repeat of No. 5; landed on Nov. 17 on Soviet territory. |

# Index

**177**